Reviews

THE UNLIKELY VICTIMS

When reading this first rate mystery, one might think that this story will be character driven and will short change the setting. However the opening paragraph sets the scene. The author uses beautiful language and creates haunting images fulfilling the reader's thirst for vividly painted backdrop against which the characters can play out their dramas.

Victoria Lorrekovich, U.S.A.

I loved the ending. How powerful! It's so true in life that we end up crossing paths with people in ways that defy logic and truly make us feel the presence of a Higher Power orchestrating it all. All of your stories bring this point home and have a very positive perspective as well as being entertaining with excellent twists. You truly are gifted – can't wait for more. I'm passing the book among my friends, so you'll have a following in the New York area.

Marjorie Lang, U.S.A.

WHY, ZAIDA?

The Canadian Jewish News: Toronto, Ontario

The book *"Why, Zaida?"* by Alvin Abram, illustrated by Judy Willemsma, talks about that kind of person – a grandfather who talks about the Holocaust only after his grandson asks and asks. Nevertheless, the grandfather has to answer his grandson. He does this with the time-honoured technique of parables, stories that help teach a lesson – a robin eating a worm, a dog chasing a squirrel, a leaf caught in a stream, a grassy bank. Every page has beautiful illustrations in lush greens, blues and browns.

Leila Speisman

Jewish Free Press: Calgary, Alberta

Author uses metaphors from nature to explain the Holocaust. Why, Zaida? explains the brutality of the unnamed Nazi regime and its collaborators by drawing another analogy as they see a dog attempting to prey on a squirrel. Likewise, he likens evil to weeds, which threatens the good grass if left unchecked. Alvin Abram's sensitive exploration is beautifully illustrated by Judy Willemsma. Interspersed with illustrations and text are the Yiddish words for *Why, Zaida?* . . . Abram generalizes the story – perhaps to provide a gentler, more universal approach to young readers first being introduced to the potentially traumatic subject matter.

Maxine Fischbein

STORIES I WROTE

The Eugene Joseph Story: For the most part, the words never got in the way of the story. This is more difficult than it sounds. The writer has an obvious, natural gift for narrative. I was never lost.

Philip G. Schloss, U.S.A

Touched by Love: The author's short story of love, choices and honest truth will fill your heart with emotion. By the second paragraph you will be connected to the characters and not only care what happens to them but you will be awaiting their next move with anticipation. The author allows the reader to visualize the events as they unfold and lets you into their lives. The beautiful relationship that is portrayed in this story is the best I have read in a long time.

Miriam Porter: Producer/Actor, Canada

Touched by Love: A thoughtfully written piece about an unexpected pregnancy and the parallel love between a man and a woman told from a male perspective.

Sasha Nicole, U.S.A.

Road Rage: What a keen sense of perception. A vivid picture in the mind's eye with which anyone who ever felt at their wit's end can identify. The author places the reader right in the car, embroiled in the emotional suspense, then expand the character's humanness before adding the final twist of irony. A must-read, thought provoking page turner.

Marjorie Lang, U.S.A.

Road Rage: Married to her for twenty years and nagged by her for ten, this dull man found a way of tuning his wife out. He had allowed a boring life full of 'yes dears' to fill him with hatred. His feeble excuses, 'I am no social animal' and 'I am too tired,' had driven her to seek attention by driving him crazy. Was he just lost on his way to her sister's or had he lost the plot of his life – a realistic story with a twisted ending.

Susanna Weiner, England

A Stitch in Time: It was easy to visualize the dynamics between the mother and the son. I felt I was in the room with them. The scene also took me back to a vivid scene in my own memory . . . which made me smile and cry. Nice story!

Gloria Claman, Canada

Forbidden: I was impressed with this original love story most forbidden, but so vivid and exotic, between a Jewish woman and a gentile.

Arie Shevy-Shibi, Israel

Forgive Me: I believe that this particular writer is destined for greatness and must pursue his ability to achieve these ends.

Michael Goatham, U.S.A.

Kugler: A very good story overall. Wonderful usage of actual events. Definitely a very good understanding of history as shown by how elements were added to the work. Brought a few tears and a sniffle upon first reading.

Ashley Lange, U.S.A.

Flight: You tell a good story. It's intriguing and makes one want to keep reading. I liked how you moved back and forth in time. That builds interest.

Terry Ward, U.S.A.

The Credit Card Caper: I found to be a quickly engaging story with a nice easy flow. The characters were well portrayed, the plot is smooth and clean, the humour is fun!

Carolyn Nielsom, U.S.A.

Jonas: The Baker: The best I've read anywhere for a long time. It was an absolute joy to read. Sir, you are an excellent writer.

Mike West, U.S.A.

Ta-Ta-T-A-Ta: I have to say I really like your prose. It has a maturity that's refreshing to see. Your opening is nice, setting the mood, the loneliness, fear, reluctance of the situation at hand.

Clair Anderson, U.S.A.

THE LIGHT AFTER THE DARK I and II
Afterword: As I walk home from Indigo [Book Store] in mid-town Toronto on a chilly Sunday November, I am overwhelmed with emotion. It is Holocaust Week and author/storyteller Alvin Abram spoke to the bookstore crowd. Only his friendly eyes and easy-going disposition match his mesmerizing voice. Abram's stories of chance and circumstance deal with the miracles of the Holocaust and child survivors, and his dedication to inform and spread awareness inspires me.

Miriam Porter: Producer/actor
Excerpt from an article: The Past Can Inspire the Future

The Canadian Jewish News: The six stories from the Holocaust in this volume are unusual and engrossing. Like many others of a similar nature, they contain much that is appalling and evil, a degradation of the spirit. But they are also a testimony to human fortitude, hope, courage and inspiration. Out of the darkness came forth light and out of despair flowed renewal and redemption. Alvin Abram has fashioned a book to be cherished. It both nourishes and enlarges the spirit.

Rabbi Bernard Baskin

These are powerful stories and for the most part you have told them well. In a marketplace that is crowded with Holocaust manuscripts, I think yours stands out . . . I was initially dubious about the Holocaust conveyed by means of something fictionalized short narratives, but the result is a powerful manuscript, so how can I argue against the basic premise. This is one of the best Holocaust manuscripts I've read.

Greg Ioannou
Manuscript Evaluator, Toronto, Canada

I found the two stories that I read to be emotionally disturbing . . . graphic detail left little to the imagination. As you pointed out, one story had been video taped and in all probability your summary has more detail because of the time spent acquiring the information. When reading your version, I found it had a different impact than hearing the person relating their experiences.

Janet Klein Slavin
The Survivors of the Shoah Visual History Foundation, Toronto, Canada

Before hunger, deprivation, terror and torture, there was another kind of life – life filled with meaning, spirituality, dignity, resistance and struggle that, even in the blackest moment in the history of the Jewish people, the enemy could neither vanquish nor destroy. That is the message of this powerful, moving book, a message we must never forget.

Professor Irving Abella
Co-author of None Is Too Many: Canada and the Jews of Europe 1933-1948
with Harold Troper

The Jewish Post & News: Winnipeg, Manitoba: These stories enlarge our understanding of both history and humanity. Irving Abella writes that books like this one are profoundly important. I agree. This testimony is powerful and moving – a most worthwhile read.

Bob Hawkins

Jerusalem Post: Jerusalem, Israel: We knew her as The General and made fun of her. But we didn't know, we didn't know. The incredible tale of Batia Malamud is told in a recent book by Alvin Abram . . . This old woman, the butt of indignity on Prince Charles Street, was the greatest hero we ever met. And we never knew.

Sam Orbaum

The Leader Post: Regina, Saskatchewan: Abram relates true-life accounts of men and women who lived through the Holocaust . . . Abram collected and published these poignant and inspiring stories in hopes that they would change the perspective of people who hear them.

Nick Miliokas

About the Author

ABRAM is a storyteller, writer and graphic designer of books. He returned to the dream of his youth in 1995, attending York University Creative Fourth Year Writing Course, followed by an Outline Course in 1996 at University of Toronto, finishing with a Creative Summer Writing Course in 1997 at Humber College. He refined his craft of listening to stories, gleaning first hand knowledge and insight from their experiences, knowing how to keep an audience interested and entertained by telling his tales with a passion for the events he unfolds. He has had almost one hundred speaking engagements since 1995.

ABRAM self-published in 1997 a 244-page hard cover book, *The Light After the Dark*, six unusual true stories of children who had experiences during the Holocaust that defied logic. Re-published by Key Porter Books in 1998. The royalties are being donated to Jewish charities.

ABRAM self-published in 2000, *Why, Zaida?* A coloured, fully illustrated hard cover fiction story of a nine-year-old boy asking his grandfather why he has no father or mother. The grandfather uses a squirrel, a dog, a robin, a stick and stream, grass and weeds as metaphors to answer him.

ABRAM self-published in 2001, *The Light After the Dark II*, a 271-page book with additional true stories of children who had experiences during the Holocaust that defied logic.

ABRAM self-published in 2002, *The Unlikely Victims*, a 244-page book about a Jewish homicide detective, Gabe Garshowitz, in Toronto who becomes involved in six fictional cases. Nominated for the Arthur Ellis Award for the Best First Novel in 2002 by Crime Writers of Canada.

ABRAM has had thirty short stories and articles published between 1997 and 2003 in *Wordscape Mystery Anthologies, Women's World* (New York), *Winners' Circle, Chicken Soup for the Parent's Soul, North York Post, Bayview Post, The Israeli Magazine, Canadian Jewish News* and others. He has appeared on television, radio and has been interviewed and reviewed in newspapers throughout Canada, U.S. and Israel.

ABRAM continues to write. He has completed a novella, *A Bone to Pick*, a Gabe Garshowitz mystery as well as two new murder mystery/love stories entitled *An Eye For An Eye* and *The Minyan*. Is working on another murder mystery novel . . . *And The Beat Goes On*, another Gabe Garshowitz novel.

ABRAM is a volunteer in the Toronto Jewish community, Vice President of the Jewish National Fund (Toronto), member of Crime Writers of Canada and Writers Union of Canada

Stories I Wrote

by
ALVIN ABRAM

AMA_Graphics_ Incorporated
Toronto   Ontario   Canada

Stories I Wrote
Copyright @ 2003 by Alvin Abram

Some of the stories in this collection were originally published as follows:

"Ta-Ta-T-A-Ta", "Stitch in Time", "A Story in Two Words"
in Wordscape Mystery Anthology 4 (1997)

"Jonas: The Baker" in Winner's Circle (1998)

"The Coat That Wouldn't Die"
in The Canadian Jewish News (1998)
and North York Post (1999) and Thornhill Post (1999)

"The Credit Card Caper" in Wordscape Mystery Anthology 6 (1999)

"Remember: Come Home" in Fraternally Yours (1999)

"The Photograph Album"
in Chicken Soup for the Parent's Soul (2000) and
Women's World Magazine (New York) (2001)

"Kugler", "Touched by Love", "Forgive Me"
in New Generation (2001)

"The Harvey Shulman Case" in The Unlikely Victims (2002)

Special thanks to Eugene Joseph for permission to reprint
his memoirs The Memories I Live With (2002)

National Library of Canada Cataloguing in Publication

Alvin Abram, 1936-
Stories I Wrote / by Alvin Abram

ISBN 0-9733480-0-3

I. Title

PS8551.B49S86 2003   C813'.6   C2003-903650-2

Published by AMA Graphics Incorporated
Toronto, Ontario, Canada

Cover, page design and typesetting by
Charlotte Launø

Printed in Canada

To my co-author
my partner
my heart
my wife

Marilyn

There are a number of people who made this book possible,
whose inspiration, input and talent helped mould
the images in my head into words on paper

Maryan Gibson, editor

Myrna Riback, editor

Professor Matthew Corrigan, York University Creative Writing

the many reviewers
from Francis Coppola's Zoetrope Web Site

and

JoAnn Gold
for her sharp eyes and kind words

Table of Contents

SECTION THREE: *Stories About People*

Section One:

Stories from the Heart

A Stitch In Time

THE ROOM APPEARED the same, but it wasn't. Nothing had changed. The furniture was in the same place, pictures on the walls, carpets, stool, lamps all there, even the sewing machine. Everything but her. She was in a Home for the Aged, too old to live alone.

I remember, as if it were yesterday, sitting on the couch opposite her while she worked on someone's dress. My mother was small in stature and had a hump on her back from spending a lifetime bent over many sewing machines. She was unaware that I had been staring at her over my book for several minutes. I listened to the machine as it attacked the fabric, her legs, synchronized in perfect rhythm, pumped the treadle, making the sewing machine sing. Her fingers danced with such lightness, darting over and around, as if daring the needle to strike her. The lines on her face were deeply etched, her concentration fully focused on what she was doing.

I returned to my book, but the words were a blur, and finally I placed my bookmark inside and closed it. Books were my escape, a place where I could dream. When I looked at my mother, I wondered, do mothers dream? Her foot stopped, she heaved a big sigh and flexed her fingers. I waited to see if she was finished. Within seconds, her foot moved again and the material continued to weave its way over and around the table.

I wondered about her age. She must be . . . at least fifty, maybe fifty-one. She had always appeared so young, a clean, fresh look with a trace of vanilla following her, and a laughing smile. A twinkle would appear in her eyes when she related a tale from her days in Europe, always holding back the punch line until she had attained the right amount of suspense. She was only five-foot-six, and yet I never got the impression that I was looking down at her. As I watched her then, I noticed how small she was, the lines under her eyes, the sprinkling of gray in her pitch-black hair, the exaggerated slouch of her body. It was as if the changes had occurred overnight.

As a teenager, I lived in two worlds of make-believe. One I created for myself with my books and one my mother fabricated, so I would never realize we were poor. I never felt our poverty until I was invited to my friends' homes, then I saw the difference.

Our family survived on my mother's toil, as she suffocated in a sweat factory by day and freelanced as a seamstress at night, and yet she never complained. She would say: never ask for more than you need. To take and not use is to hurt others who have a bigger need. What bigger need, I asked myself, than your own? And why not have more? It wasn't until years later I realized what she meant. We should be grateful for what we had, because others had less, and yet, I thought we had hardly anything. Except love that is. A limitless bounty of love.

Silent.

Unspoken.

Only felt.

The sewing machine stopped again. She slowly eased herself from her chair. I saw the pain in her eyes. She looked at me and smiled. "Good book?" she asked, reaching for the broom to sweep the floor.

"Yes."

"Jewish?"

"No. Science fiction."

She nodded her head as if she understood and I smiled to myself. To my mother, everyone and everything was Jewish.

"Would you like some Jell-O and cookies?" she asked.

"I saw the Jell-O. Where did you hide the cookies?"

She smiled. "Some place so obvious you wouldn't think to look."

For entertainment, my friends had something called television, but I had my mother and her sense of humour. "How do you know I looked?" I asked.

Her smile broadened. "You looked."

"You're too smart. Where did you hide the cookies?"

"When trying to solve a problem, most times the answer is right under your nose."

I glanced down at the table before me.

"No, no. Think. Where didn't you look?" She patted her dress down, smoothing out the wrinkles, then met my gaze again. "Have you figured it out?"

"In my room?"

"Of course. Why would you expect to find what you want in your own room?"

I ran to my bedroom and pulled out the dresser drawers until I discovered the Arrowroot cookies hidden under my shirts. I returned to the kitchen.

My mother was standing in front of the icebox.

She hadn't seen me yet.

She was slumped forward, resting with one arm on the edge of the open door.

She appeared so tired.

So old.

Why did she have to grow old?

Midnight
Madness

I AM NOT a domesticated husband. I am not a chauvinist, just a borderline *clotz*. I have a tendency to forget what I am suppose to do. I never go shopping and Marilyn never asks. But a few years ago, Marilyn asked if I would come Passover shopping with her. Not just Passover shopping, but after eight in the evening at the old Sunnybrook Market for what was being billed as Midnight Madness. It went against her promise, but her reason was that it required two to shop on this particular night.

When we approached the entrance, Marilyn grabbed my arm and pointed to two deserted buggies tucked into each other. "Quick, grab that buggy." Her normally serene voice hinted of panic. Unfortunately, I was unable to separate the two buggies. "Never mind, never mind," she pleaded, "I see another," and ran inside the building to a lonely buggy that had just been discarded by its previous owner. "Oh my God," she exclaimed, all the good stuff will be gone. Follow me," and plunged down the outside aisle into the noisy mass of clamoring people.

"Follow me!"

Before me was a narrow aisle packed with bodies of tall and small, old, young and fat. In the centre of the aisle were several tables filled with an assortment of chocolates and other items. On both sides of the tables, tight against the shelves to the exterior wall, was a slow, hardly moving sea of humanity, most of whom were pushing oversized buggies, as they examined, smelled, squeezed and discussed the items in their hands. Moses could never have parted these bodies even with the help of divine providence.

I made a terrible mistake. I blinked my eyes in shock and, in that interval, Marilyn disappeared. Those behind me nudged me forward against my will. Hands crossed before my eyes as they stretched to the shelf or the tables, plucking their selection from the mountain of goodies surrounding me as would the Canada Arm on the American spacecraft. This was not the place for a non-aggressive person. A few times my carriage got caught in someone else's or I was hit from behind by kamikaze drivers. A hand waved and Marilyn appeared ahead of me, beckoning. I zig-zagged around the human obstacles, begged my pardon and made my way to her. Marilyn held in her arms the beginning of her madness purchases.

Enclossed on four sides by a wedge of bodies, I was rooted to a fixed spot as items flew into my buggy. When Marilyn was finished, she disappeared again. I saw an opening and tried to manoeuvre forward. A heavily built woman came alongside me and the packed bodies parted to allow her access. I pulled in behind her, allowing her to cleave a passage, until we reached the bottom of the aisle where I tucked myself into a corner and waited for Marilyn to find me. She approached with her arms filled with an assortment of candies, marshmallows, chocolates and God-knows-what and unceremoniously dumped them into the buggy, then turned the corner to an aisle filled with even more people.

Across from me, a deserted aisle ran back towards the entrance and I quickly pushed my way into the aisle of calm. Others, seeing me enter, followed, only to discover the aisle contained no Passover items, and tried to back out again into the flow of people, causing a lumberjack's nightmare. A wave of bodies pushed by and I gazed at the bobbing heads from my place of safety, ignored by the passing madness that had betaken normal people.

A woman passed. Stopped. She looked into my buggy and snatched an item lying amidst the small mountain of goods. "Where did you get this?" she demanded, as her eyes darted about, searching for it on a nearby shelf. She extended her arm holding the item into my face.

I pointed back where Marilyn had been. The woman dropped the package and plunged into the sea of bodies. I hovered over my possessions in a protective stance.

Ten minutes passed. I was concerned Marilyn might have forgotten where I was parked and reluctantly I pushed my buggy back into the stream of people. The volume from the hundreds of voices squeezed into this ravine of merchandise was as loud as water cascading down Niagara Falls and I was feeling all the symptoms of a gigantic migraine.

On my right was a 'dead spot' leading into a room behind strips of thick plastic. I inched my way over there and parked the buggy. I saw Marilyn. I raised my six-feet-three-inch height onto my toes hoping she would see me over the bobbing heads. She did not.

Barreling along was someone I had known for twenty years. His hair was disarranged and on his face a look of someone obsessed with a mission. He stopped not more than fifteen feet from me, scooped something off the shelf, his eyes swinging like a pendulum, trying to focus on everything without giving up the ground he had staked out. I shouted his name. "Stuart! Stuart!" He stared at me as if I were an invader, smiled, which for him can be an effort, and disappeared into another aisle in pursuit of more items on the piece of paper clutched in his hand.

An elderly lady tucked herself beside me. "It's *mishiggah*," she said and quickly left.

Marilyn found me and dropped off her next load of contraband, disappearing without a 'by your leave' to bob and weave to other items. My pain came to an end when Marilyn threw the last items into the crammed buggy and we forged ahead to the lines waiting for check-out. I watched $300.00 change ownership. Marilyn wanted to go to another store. Not next door, but one on the corner of Steeles and Bathurst. By now my migraine was having a headache.

That store was relatively empty. Marilyn led me up one aisle and down another.

"One more thing," she said.

I breathed a sigh of relief.

"Finished," Marilyn said as she plunked the last container into the buggy.

Relieved, I turned my buggy to the check out line. With the shopping finally finished (over two hours had passed) we returned home. I had been lucky to add only one box of *mandelbread* and one box of coconut marshmallows to the list without Marilyn being aware. Comfortably sitting in front of my computer, an open box of coconut marshmallows hidden under a pile of papers, I heard Marilyn bellowing my name. She claimed four items were missing. I insisted I had seen them being packed. Marilyn insisted they were missing. A search of the house and the car resulted in the return of my headache – not the missing items.

Cash register tape in one hand and my car keys in the other, Marilyn was returning to the second store where the items were purchased. As a parting jab, I said, "Try the buggy. I put it back in the rack in the parking lot," not really believing what I suggested. A half hour later, Marilyn returned with the missing four items. They were in the buggy, in the rack, but by then were four buggies into the chain and she had to get help to reach them.

Is there a morale to this tale?

No!

She said she would never ask me to shop with her again but I don't believe her. She had said that thirty years ago and didn't keep her word.

Touched By Love

ONLY A FEW hours had passed, a long few hours, since I had learned that my wife was pregnant. I'd taken her in my arms and hugged her, but it was not happiness that I felt. In the early years of our marriage, I would have met her news with genuine enthusiasm, but now, after twenty-five years . . . I was forty-nine, she, forty-three.

The words almost gagged in my throat when I said them. "What about having an abortion?" I saw the pain in her eyes as if the words had struck her. Never would I have believed I would say such a thing. I loved life, loved being alive, and now my thoughts were of death, the death of someone not yet born. "Damn!" I railed. "Why did I say that?" I buried my face in my hands.

I rose to my feet and paced the room. Like a caged animal, I prowled between the furniture, wanting to erase the words that wouldn't go away. Ours was a good marriage and – for many reasons – one, the three children we'd had and loved. We'd wanted more, but want and have were not always consistent with time and effort . . . and now, so many years later . . . I didn't think I wanted another child.

We'd talked about the risks, especially since she'd had two miscarriages when she was younger. Her age was certainly a factor. That more than anything frightened me. That was when I suggested having an abortion. The words had escaped and, although I hadn't pressed the issue, there was an undercurrent of tension between us as soon as they were uttered.

She had made an appointment with her gynaecologist. I stayed home to wrestle with my thoughts. Time, I thought, where had it gone? The days of our youth had seemed so endless. It was as if I'd married her only yesterday. What a sad word, 'yesterday.' There were more yesterdays than tomorrows left for us and now she wanted to gamble with what was left. Did I? Within a few years, our children would be leaving and going on their own. It was a freedom I had looked forward to. The future was ours to enjoy – if I didn't accept parenthood again when I became fifty.

I heard her car on the driveway. I closed my eyes for a brief moment as I tried to calm my mind. There was no more time left. Whatever way this went, there was risk involved; it was not just her health I needed to consider, but our relationship. What to do with the baby? I didn't know. Try as I could, I found no feelings within me to offer an answer. Did I love her? That was an easier question to answer. The earlier years of our marriage had been difficult as we learned about each other. Learned what love meant. Learned to be partners instead of participants. Learned each other's needs. Ours was more than a marriage – we had become friends.

I went to meet her when she entered the house. We both smiled, but the smiles were contrived and disappeared quickly. I could see she'd been crying. Obviously she, too, was still struggling with the question.

"Do you want the baby?" I asked.

She nodded.

The lines of worry on my face softened and I smiled, a genuine smile. "Then let's go for it."

She threw her arms around my neck and hugged me while I prayed we'd made the right decision. Still holding her waist, I pushed her away and added, "On the condition that I don't have to come into the delivery room."

She laughed as the tears ran down her cheeks. "Chicken," she said, and hugged me harder.

Each day that passed, I suffered over my decision. I watched her closely for any signs of trouble, any indication that our decision was not the right one, but none occurred. "How are you feeling?" I repeatedly asked, unable to hide my concern.

Her answer was always reassuring. "I'm fine. Stop worrying."

I would telephone her at work and ask if there were any problems, and she would laugh, saying, "You worry too much." Everything seemed to be following its normal course. As the days turned into weeks, I saw her eyes sparkle with excitement at what was growing in her body, marvelled as she gently caressed her still-flat belly, her hands shaping the imaginary size it would grow.

"What do you want?" she asked. "A boy or a girl?"

I smiled and took her hands. "What do you want?"

"Another boy. What do you think?"

"That would be nice," I answered, hugging her close. "Just as long as your health isn't affected."

My fears waned, to be replaced by pride and confidence and I began to relax, feeling the worst was over. But it wasn't. Three months into the pregnancy, she telephoned me one morning at my office. Her voice was strained.

"I don't feel well," she said.

My whole body went cold. "Do you want to go to the hospital?"

"I don't know. I'm not sure."

"Did you call your doctor?"

"No. I called you first."

"Call him, then call me back?"

"I will."

I waited by the phone, my heart beating fast, my mind jumping from one scenario to another – all bad. My hand rested on the telephone, trying to sense the second it would come to life. And when it did, I snatched it up. "What did he say?"

"To come down right away."

"I'll be there in twenty minutes and take you."

"I'll be all right. I'm sure it's nothing. My friend Barbara will take me. She's here now. I'll be hours and you have several important appointments. I'm to have an ultrasound test and God knows what. Barbara will drop me off at your office and we'll go home together. I'll be all right."

"All right," I answered reluctantly.

WHEN SHE ARRIVED at my office, I still wasn't back from my appointments, so she settled into my guest chair to wait. It had been a long day of waiting. After her tests, the nurse said they were backlogged and she should go home. She would call her later with the results. She had smiled, giving reassurances. Each time the telephone rang, she hoped it would be me, but it was someone else. Then it did ring for her. She smiled with anticipation, but the caller was the nurse from the doctor's office.

"Thank God, I found you!" she said. "I tried your house and took a chance on you being at your husband's office. The results of your tests show an ectopic pregnancy – the fetus is implanted in a fallopian tube, where it can't develop. You could be hemorrhaging. You must return to the hospital immediately. The doctor will be waiting for you."

She paled. "All right," she whispered, then hung up.

Shaken, she asked my secretary for a list of my calls and telephoned several clients looking for me, but to no avail. She didn't want to go to the hospital without me. As time went by, concern made her look out the window every few minutes, hoping I might walk in. Finally, two hours later, I did.

SHE ASKED ME to take her home first to pick up some personal items. From the house I bundled her into the front seat of my car and drove frantically to the hospital. It was almost five o'clock and traffic was horrendous. My concern for her increased when I noticed her pallor and shallow breathing. I regretted taking her home and not calling an ambulance when I had returned to the office. As the minutes ticked by, my mistake took on dire consequences. More than ever, I regretted not calling my office to find out if she had arrived. I had got caught up in my appointments and had forgotten about her – a major error in judgment that might jeopardize her life! When the hospital was only a block away, I turned to tell her we were almost there. She didn't respond. She was sagging heavily against the door and her eyes were closed.

I pulled into the emergency entrance and ran for help. Attendants and nurses rushed to my aid, placed her on a gurney and wheeled her into the building and out of sight. As I stood in the corridor watching their rapid departure, fear smothered me and I started to cry.

A nurse touched my shoulder. She smiled. "She's in good hands," she said. "Please, come with me. I'll let the doctor know where you are."

She led me into a room filled with people, but I saw no one. My wandering thoughts took me to a time when she and I had waited in a hospital for critical news about our son, drawing on each other for support. Now it was she who was in danger, and I was alone. I shook my head to rid myself of my negative thoughts and took solace in remembering happier times.

I leaned back in my chair and closed my eyes, recalling when we'd first met. I was twenty-one and she only fifteen. When she was seventeen she asked me to marry her and eighteen months later I did. We enjoyed the good times, which were many, and persevered through the difficult times, always sharing the responsibilities. Ours had been a good relationship. I opened my eyes suddenly when I realized I had thought the word 'had'. I covered my face with my hands and silently wept.

The doctor finally appeared, after three hours. "Your wife is fine," he said. "She was very lucky. Twenty more minutes and I'm not sure we could have saved her. She'd been hemorrhaging internally for some time and lost a considerable amount of blood. I'm sorry to tell you, there was no hope of saving the fetus."

My head dropped to my chest as the impact of the loss hit me. I had wanted the child. I knew that now. Now when there was no child to have, my grief tore at me. My loss weighed on my shoulders like a block of cement; I clenched my fists, regretting not recognizing my feelings earlier. I hoped her love for me was strong enough to overcome this tragedy, and that she would forgive me for not putting her concerns first.

The doctor saw the look on my face and misunderstood. "She's fine," he assured me. "With rest and care, she'll be as good as ever."

"Can I see her?"

"She's sedated. She won't wake up for a while."

"Can I sit in her room?"

The doctor nodded. "Yes, of course."

A nurse took me to her room. I entered hesitantly. A small bulb from a ceiling fixture cast a light over her head and made strange shadows on the walls. The IV bottle was suspended from a hook beside the narrow bed and a machine beeped in the background, a red light blinked on and off. She lay on her back, pale and very still, her eyes closed. Only the slight movement of the cover over her chest as she breathed gave any indication she was alive. God, she looked so small, so fragile, I thought.

I pushed a chair to the side of the bed and gazed at her still form. I sat rigidly against the back of the chair, my gaze focused on her outline on the bed, and listened to the beep of the machine. Would she understand my not calling the office?

By eleven, my eyes began to close. I sensed her breathing; the beeping of the machine slowly faded from my consciousness. I was on the verge of falling asleep when she spoke.

"Hi," she said softly.

I opened my eyes and saw she was smiling. I smiled back. "Hi."

"I won."

"Won? Won what?" I asked.

Her smile broadened. "As they wheeled me into the operating room, I made a bet with myself, and I won the bet."

She reached for my hand and placed it over hers, locking our fingers.

"I don't understand. What kind of a bet?" I asked.

"I bet, when I awoke, my best friend would be in the room with me – and you are."

It's Never Too Late To Dream

I LOOKED AT the doctor, fighting back my tears. I had hoped that when I met with him, the news I would hear would at least offer me some hope, but what I heard was as bad as it could be. We stared at each other, the silence hanging heavily in the air, and neither one of us appeared prepared to break it.

I dropped my gaze to my hands, the first tear slowly slipping down my cheek. "Is there any kind of medicine that might make a difference?" I whispered.

"No, I'm sorry, there isn't. If there were, I would have recommended it."

"How long?"

"It varies – a few years at least. There'll be a steady decline in health. You've already seen some of it. It will become more obvious as time passes."

"And now . . . what do I do now?"

"Your mother can't live alone anymore. She needs twenty-four hour care. What you've done until now was fine, but it's time for the next stage. You knew this day would come."

"I've made believe it wouldn't. What you're asking of me will kill her."

"She's already dying. You have to come to grips with that. What she has is a progressive illness without any known cure, at least not as of this moment."

My voice trembled. "It's not fair. I'm not ready."

"Is anyone ever?"

"I wish I could turn the clock back. Would you believe I've never told her how much I love her."

"Tell her now," he said.

I shook my head. "If I say it now – she can't hear me."

"You don't know that."

"Do you?"

"No."

I stood.

The doctor pushed several sheets of papers toward me. "These are the places I would recommend. My advice is to move on this quickly."

I shuffled the sheets together and folded them, placing them in my inside suit pocket. "Tomorrow," I said. "Now I have to see her and tell her what must be done."

"She won't understand," the doctor said. "She's beyond that. You know that."

I nodded and left his office.

I SAT IN my car outside my mother's apartment building, unwilling to enter, knowing what awaited me. It was reassuring to see the sun's twilight rays on the autumn leaves, to appreciate the flow of nature and accept that all life inevitably must come to an end. And yet, as I gazed up at my mother's apartment window, I could not appreciate what life had done to her.

Sitting in my car offered me temporary relief, but I knew I could not put off entering her building. No matter how long I sat, the inevitable still waited for me. I had made excuses for what I was seeing. I refused to accept the truth, but the truth refused to go away. In my eyes, my mother appeared ageless, but the realities of the present had awakened me to the knowledge that time does not stand still, and what I saw could no longer be ignored. Her doctor warned me a year ago, but hope had a way of making me ignore the tell-tale signs.

I looked down at my hands and turned them over slowly. She used to hold my hands when she was talking about something serious. European-born with simple old country logic, she was my friend and protector as I grew up. When I lived at home, I would go into my room that I shared with a younger brother, close the door and bury myself in a book for the sheer pleasure of being someplace else. My room was very small; the four cracked, plaster walls enclosed my sanctuary – it was my universe. My mother sensed it was where I hid from the pain and difficulty of growing up in a home that was not stable. She was a good mother, but she never spoke the word 'love' and yet I never felt unloved. Whatever I became, I owed to her and now when she could use my help, I felt helpless.

I left my car and slowly went through the front door of the building. I approached the elevator, grateful it was positioned on the top floor. It gave me more time before I had to face her. The elevator door opened and I reluctantly entered its sterile interior, my thoughts on the past, not the present. There were times when I would invent reasons to come to her building – to inhale the aroma of her cooking, to listen to the no-nonsense conversation from someone I admired and respected. She loved nature, loved to make things grow and loved life. I saw the changes in her, but made excuses. Her apartment took on the appearance of neglect; her clothes were unwashed and her conversation became increasingly stinted and broken.

The elevator stopped and I stepped into the carpeted hall, then headed towards her door. Beside her door was a mezuzah to bless those who entered, but I did not feel blessed by what would confront me. Her home always rang with laughter and all around the walls hung souvenirs of my brothers' and my childhood. It was a sanctuary where I could bare my grief and know she would kiss away my pain and make me feel better. To visit my mother's apartment as an adult was to feel young again. She fed me meals made from recipes handed down from one generation to the next, meals that could not be found anywhere else exactly the way she made them. Her home was filled with good memories, but now I hesitated at the door – not wanting to enter.

I knocked, even though I had a key, praying she would greet me with that familiar twinkle in her eyes. I listened for sounds of movement, but all was silent. I placed the key in the lock and opened the door. The electric lights were off, but the sun's rays shone through the window, bathing the room in natural light. She was sitting on the edge of the couch wearing her nightgown and housecoat, her hands clasped in front of her, her head bowed. I prayed she would turn her eyes towards me, but she appeared unaware of my presence. The woman I hired to be with her had gone home. I was late that night.

"Hello, Mom. How are you?"

She did not answer.

I forced myself to move closer. The light from outside her window faded as if to hide her. I turned on the lamp. Still she showed no sign that she was aware of my presence. She sat in a room surrounded by her past, a past she no longer remembered. The walls were hung with pictures and plates, each with a story she could no longer tell. There were scratches on the furniture I was responsible for, the sculpture on the floor with a chip on it, broken by one of my brothers, the carving of a chest made by another brother – all loved, all cherished, now only objects without history, without love.

I began the ritual of my visit by telling of her my day's activities. I told her about her grandchildren, that her other sons would come tomorrow, that soon she would be a great-grandmother. Her eyes blinked and a tear formed. I couldn't find the words to tell her what the doctor had said. The words choked in my throat and I couldn't release them.

I had arranged for a woman to keep my mother company, to care, feed and prevent her from doing herself harm during the day. The woman, however, never made much of an effort to keep the apartment clean. There was an odour of decayed food coming from somewhere. I rose and began to clean the room. I felt my mother's eyes following me. I looked for the source of the odour, finally locating the rotting food in the knitting basket she no longer used.

I returned to her side.

She looked at me and smiled, and I smiled back.

"Where's my mother?" she asked.

"She's gone out for a little while," I answered.

"Why didn't she stay with me?"

"She'll be back soon. Don't worry."

Each time I came, I heard the same questions. I clasped both her hands with mine, hoping all her confusion would seep through her fingers where I could dispel it. I felt the pressure of her fingers on my hands; her skin was tough as leather, creased and marked by the many hours she had worked on her sewing machine. The look on her face did not change. I waited for the next question.

"Do you know my mother?" she asked.

"No, but I know a lot about her. She's a nice person, just like you."

She nodded. Her eyes were not on me when I spoke and I wondered if she knew what I had just said.

"Who are you?"

"I'm your son."

She stared at me. "Do we know each other?"

"Yes, very well."

The smile slipped from her face. I knew I was losing her again. I held her hands for a little while longer before telling her I had to leave.

She raised her head and looked at me, but there was no recognition in her eyes. I led her to her bed and removed her housecoat, covered her with the comforter, leaned over, kissed her good night and headed for the door. But then I stopped to look back at her. She lay still, lifeless, looking so fragile. Time no longer existed for her. At least not the time I knew.

As a young girl in Romania, Annie loved to run in foot races, which despite competing against taller girls, she usually won. It was more than her natural ability, however, it was her positive attitude. She believed that, with an abundance of desire and common sense, a sprinkle of determination and a pinch of luck thrown in for good measure, nothing was impossible.

She was twenty-two when she arrived in Canada, carrying a small suitcase and big dreams – dreams of a bright future in a promising new land. She always carried her small body with dignity. Later when her back became slightly hunched, people didn't notice it because her smile absorbed their attention. She always wore high-heeled shoes to show off her legs, about which she was quite vain. "God makes everyone beautiful," she would say, "but not always in places that are easy to appreciate."

It was the era of the Great Depression, when workers were considered no better than chattel and machines were held in high regard. Annie found work as a seamstress in a large clothing manufacturing company, where she arrived before sunrise and worked under conditions that tested her physical endurance. With the skill of an experienced craftsman, her sure fingers guided a steady succession of garments through her machine. Covered in perspiration from the heat of the nearby pressing machines, Annie worked long hours in a poorly ventilated room. Her temporary comfort was the handkerchief tied around her neck to absorb the perspiration that dripped from her face. In reality, she was a slave to her machine, but in her eyes she was building the foundation for a better life. Always a patient person, Annie persevered.

She met Herman, fell in love, and their marriage gave them three sons. Murray was the firstborn, followed by me, and then Morton. The family rarely had enough money to make ends meet and there were many times when the stress and strain of being poor added pressure to the marriage. But Annie built her life around her husband and children, devoting herself to her greatest enjoyment – being a wife and mother.

Annie had a talent for making a little into a lot – especially when it came to preparing meals. She would create the supper around a large pot of soup; into it would go vegetables, small pieces of chicken, herbs and leftovers. The aroma was delicious and empty stomachs were soon filled. Her sons never felt their poverty.

Her husband rarely earned enough to support his family, so Annie provided the primary source of income. As a piece-work operator, she made only a modest wage, so for her to earn enough money for her family's needs, a lot of garments had to pass through her machine. She worked twelve hours a day, six days a week, but never complained, for what she was doing was for her family and only that was important.

When her earnings didn't cover all the expenses, she took on a second job. In good times, she would knit her sons socks with large multi-coloured diamond designs, vests and sweaters with difficult patterns that only she knew how to create and, on special occasions, she would make herself a dress. She considered herself fortunate; her children were healthy, she had a job and her husband would someday be the person he wanted to be. "Life is good," she was known to say. "How much better could it be?"

When I was ten, I remember asking her, "Ma, my friends drink pop at home. You never bring home any pop for us. How come?"

"Why do you need pop?" she answered. "I'll make you a drink that's better than pop." She proceeded to boil water in a kettle, poured some into a glass and added about an inch of milk, then scooped out a spoonful of honey from a jar she always kept on hand to make her famous honey cake. She placed the honey in the glass and mixed it furiously, with a lot of theatrics, waving her arms and making little sounds as if the wind was her helper. The ingredients swirled around the glass, forming a miniature whirlpool. Fascinated, I gazed at the magic of my mother's creation. At last she pulled out the spoon, wrapped a napkin around the glass and handed it to me. "Here, drink this. Sip it slowly – it's hot. Be careful you don't burn your lips," she warned.

I raised the glass to my mouth. My eyes shone in anticipation, then closed as I savoured the sweet concoction. I licked my lips and smiled with pleasure. "That's good, Ma. I like it."

"TOMORROW," ANNIE USED to say. "There is always tomorrow." She was good at hiding her feelings, expressing only optimism to her children. Her husband, however, was the opposite. Herman expressed his frustration and anger with his hands. As the oldest, Murray often found himself subjected to the pain those hands could inflict over even small matters, magnified by the family's poverty.

Unwilling to take the abuse and the constant criticism, Murray packed his belongings in a duffel bag and left home when he was seventeen. He looked older than his years. Sprouting a pencil-style moustache, he joined the air force. After he enlisted, they discovered he was underage. Murray was discharged but he refused to return home. Instead, he hitchhiked out west.

In his absence, I became the target for my father's outbursts. Like Murray, he would strike me repeatedly about the head for the most insignificant misdemeanours. Annie would throw herself between us, screaming, "Enough!" My father would stomp away.

I had very few friends and this bothered Annie. My life was reading. I purchased paperbacks from money I earned after school selling newspapers on a street corner or working as a pin boy in the local bowling alley. I always came home late, long after supper, to do my homework or bury myself in a book.

When I was twelve, I had an after-school job running errands for a drug store. I got twenty-five cents an hour for walking the packages to the customers' homes. One day, I ran into our flat, very excited. "Ma, Mr. Koffler offered me a ten-cent-an-hour raise if I had a bicycle to make the deliveries. How much is a bicycle?"

"Too much," Annie replied. She watched the disappointment cloud my face. "Did Mr. Koffler say if *you* had a bicycle or if you *rode* a bicycle?"

"Why? If I can't buy one, what difference does it make?"

"Your brother Murray has a bicycle. He's not here, so why don't you use it?"

"But Ma, it's broken. It doesn't have any brakes and the chain keeps falling off. Besides I can't ride that bicycle – it's too big for me."

"You're sure Mr. Koffler said had a bicycle, yes?"

I thought. "Yes."

"Well," she said with a sly smile, "show Mr. Koffler the bicycle. Then you run beside it until you have enough money to fix it."

I stared at her and then grinned. I kept my job until school ended that year.

ANNIE WAS SUMMONED to my school. The teacher said that her fourteen-year-old son seemed to live in another world and never took part in activities with the other students. On more than one occasion, I would come home with a letter from the principal informing her I had received the strap for disciplinary reasons, accused of not paying attention. Annie had difficulty accepting what she was told. I now worked seven hours a day after school in a printing company, learning to be a hand compositor. After midnight, I would come home and do my homework before going to bed. This did not seem to her the behaviour of a troublemaker.

Annie knocked on my bedroom door and entered. "What happens to you when you're in class?" she asked. "I know you're not a bad boy, so something must happen that I don't know about. Do you want to tell me?"

I struggled to find an answer she would understand. "I dream about being somewhere else," I finally replied. "I make believe I'm one of the people in the book I'm reading and I'm in charge. There's adventure and everyone's my friend and I'm their hero – and there is no pain." I paused a moment. "I block out the teacher's voice until I can't hear him anymore. The teacher catches me and everyone in class laughs, and I go on report."

"Do you know that your dreams are not real?" Annie asked.

I nodded. "Yes, I know, but for a little while, they're real to me. Is that wrong?"

Annie sensed my pain. She never showed any one of her children more affection than the others. Guide your children, don't smother them, and they will learn to do for themselves. This is what she believed. At last she answered. "No . . . it's not wrong. Just as long as you know it's not real. It's a gift being able to be in one place while really being somewhere else. Many people won't understand because they've forgotten how to dream. I understand because I, too, dreamed when I was your age."

"Did you really?" My face filled with curiosity at my mother's confession.

"Yes, when I was young. I dreamed of meeting a handsome man, falling madly in love and riding horseback in the moonlight." Annie gave an embarrassed smile. "But as I got older, the dreams stopped. I never forgot them and neither should you forget yours. But it will bring you a lot of pain if you don't know how to use it. You must learn to live in today's world, as well as know when to dream. This way you can survive in both and maybe someday you will be able to use this gift so everyone can enjoy your dreams."

There was a smile on my face when she left. She had erased my pain with her words of wisdom.

WHEN ANNIE WAS fifty-three, my father died of a heart attack, leaving her with a bank account of four dollars and many debts. He had been my mother's big love. Annie resolved to bury the man she loved in keeping with the image his friends had of him. To do that she went to a finance company and borrowed the money, putting herself in debt.

By this time, Murray had returned home and was working. Morton left high school and I followed a year later. Annie was sad that her sons had to leave school, but she was having difficulty working long hours and her income was getting smaller. Times were changing and technology made many of the operations she did obsolete.

Within five years of her becoming a widow, she had married off all her sons. Murray married first but his marriage survived only two years and, after the divorce, he moved to Ottawa. Morton married next, then I. A few months before I was to be married, I came home looking as if my world had crumbled.

"*Nu.* Why the long face?" she asked.

I blurted out, "I asked Marilyn if she wanted to go to Atlantic City with me."

"You're not married," Annie said. "Why are you asking her to go with you before you're married?"

"I told Marilyn's mother we'd be going with you, cousin Pauline, Morton and his wife, just to make her feel safe about Marilyn coming."

"I didn't say I would go," Annie said, her eyes twinkling, "but I'd like to go. I've never been to Atlantic City. So Marilyn's mother said no – yes?"

I nodded.

Annie picked up the telephone and dialed. "Hello, Sara. I understand you don't want your Marilyn to go to Atlantic City with my son." She paused while Sara voiced her objections, then said, "Listen, Sara. If my son wanted to fool around with your Marilyn, he doesn't have to go to Atlantic City to do it. And besides, I'm going to be there." When the conversation ended, it was agreed that Marilyn could go.

ANNIE MADE FRIENDS easily. She went to bingo regularly; it helped pass the time. I came often for supper and she always cooked what I loved to eat. On one such occasion, she was sitting with me, watching me consume a meal of verenikas with lima bean soup and my favourite dessert of tangy lemon pie in a crumbly shell.

"Do you still dream?" she asked.

"What do you mean?"

"You once told me you used to dream you were someone else. You had adventures and were a hero. Don't you remember?"

I kept eating. I mumbled something Annie didn't catch. "What did you say?" she asked.

"Sometimes . . . but I'm too old."

"What does being older have to do with dreaming?"

"I never finished high school," I replied. "I can't write."

"What do you do with the pictures in your head?"

I didn't reply.

Annie knew I wanted to write. It was remarkable how she could get into my head and know what I was thinking. I knew her probing was not over.

AFTER VISITING MURRAY in Ottawa, Annie telephoned me on her return and ordered me to come immediately to her apartment. When

I entered, she pounced on me. "Your brother is living with a woman . . . yes?"

"Why are you asking me?"

"I smell a woman's perfume in his cupboards and the apartment is too clean."

I pondered what to say, not wanting to lie yet knowing that once my mother got her teeth into something, she never let go. "Yes, he's living with someone. She's not of our faith and he wasn't sure if you would approve."

"How long have they known each other?" Annie said more softly, now that her suspicions were confirmed.

"A few years. They love each other. She wants to convert to our faith," I added.

I could see my mother digesting what I had said. Did she approve? I never found out, but what she said was, "You tell your brother that if he loves her, he should marry her and make their apartment into a real home." She grinned. "You also tell him to bring her here so that I can meet her. I like her perfume."

For a few years, Annie became a professional babysitter to supplement her pension. Her love for children earned her a reputation that kept her very busy. Over time, she found it more difficult to move about, and the needs of the children harder to accommodate. Reluctantly she retired from the business, only to discover that many of her friends had left the building and moved elsewhere. She called me and asked that I find her a small apartment in a building where some of her friends had moved. I made the necessary arrangements. Just before moving in, I drove Annie to the new building to decide what furniture she would have to sell and which she could keep. She took a step inside the bachelorette and stopped suddenly. She began shaking her head.

"What's the matter, Ma?" I asked.

Her voice was quavering. "In Romania, I lived in a house with only one big room. In this country, I have lived in a two-bedroom apartment, a three-bedroom apartment, a rented bungalow and, after your father died, back into a two-bedroom. Now I am where I started – a single room. I have nowhere else to go. My life is over."

"Come live with my family," I pleaded. "I have lots of room."

Annie heard the fright in my voice, saw my worried look and my pleading eyes. She tried to change the mood. "And where in your house would I live? You have a small bungalow and two children."

I blurted out, "I'll build you an apartment in my basement."

Annie smiled. "A mother, you put in the cellar?"

We laughed.

Annie walked about the room and pointed to where she was going to put the couch and the table and chairs.

"Ma," I said. "Come live with us. Please."

Annie took my hands. "No," she said. "One mother can take care of three children, but three children can't take care of one mother." She had said this many times before. "And besides, when you and Marilyn have an argument and one of you brings me into it, what should I do? Take sides? I love you both too much. No. My place is here."

And there she stayed.

I WAS A constant visitor to my mother's apartment. Her common-sense logic made me reassess the artificial excuses I had convinced myself were arguments. Every so often, she would ask how my dreams were. I always gave her an answer that was funny. She would smile at me and her eyes laughed through my excuses. On one visit, I told her a secret. "Ma, I wrote a story."

"Yes."

"It's a real story. I didn't make it up. It happened after Lori's birthday."

"Yes."

"Do you want to hear it?"

"Of course. Why not?"

I pulled a few sheets out of my briefcase and cleared my throat a few times. I focused on the paper and nervously looked at my mother.

"You going to sing it or you going to read it?" she asked.

I read it and Annie listened with her eyes closed. When I was finished, she opened her eyes and said, smiling, "Not bad for someone who doesn't dream."

ANNIE HAD JUST turned seventy. "Ma, why don't you get married again?" I asked. "You're in good health and there's nothing wrong with marrying someone for companionship."

I watched the smile slowly slip from her face. She stared at me and saw the serious look on my face. "The first marriage was for love," she said. "The second will have to be for money."

I immediately responded, "All right. So what's stopping you from marrying a rich old man and having all the things you used to dream about?"

"I guess," she said, "I have never found anyone rich enough to match the love I had."

GROWING OLD CAN be graceful or complicated. Annie sought the help of different doctors, trying to find a remedy for the aches of aging, although it was probably the attention she sought more than the medicine. She didn't understand what was happening to her. She found simple tasks almost impossible to complete. All her life she had helped her children and now she was finding it hard to help herself. Her constant complaints were putting a strain on my brothers and me.

One day, while leaving the office of yet another specialist, Annie took my hand as we walked to the car and said, "I'm sorry I take so much of your time." She looked tired and her face had lost its former liveliness.

My heart was breaking. I strove for a lighter tone. "I'm really being selfish," I said. "By taking you to see all these different doctors, I'm hoping you'll remember where they are and, when it's my turn, you'll take me."

Annie laughed.

"You know, I'm the oldest living member in our family. Most of my friends are gone and, except for my children and grandchildren, I have no one to talk to anymore. If there is no one left I know, does that mean I am next?"

"Ma," I said softly, "just think positive. Nothing is written in stone."

Annie patted my arm affectionately.

I took Annie to see her younger sister who was living in a senior's home. I asked, "Would you like me to make an application for an apartment in this building?"

Without hesitating, Annie answered, "No."

"Why? It's a nice place. You will receive a hot meal every day and they will help you with your needs. Life will be easier for you."

Annie looked at me. "No, not for me."

"Why?"

"I wouldn't be happy living in this place. I can't be me here. I don't want it easier. I want to be me and I can only do that living in my own place, no matter what."

"It's not a prison."

"For me it would be."

"Will you think about it?" I pleaded.

"No. Besides, there aren't enough walls to hang all the pictures of my grandchildren. How can I tell one of them there is no room except in my heart?"

NOT LONG AFTER Annie turned eighty, she became blind in her right eye. She wanted to cook for her children, but with her poor eyesight and her failing memory, what she cooked was usually inedible. A few times she forgot to turn off the burners on the gas range and she burned herself. The noise from the radio or vacuum cleaner irritated her and she grew agitated when she had trouble buttoning her dress or trying to remember where she had put her apartment keys.

Too often, the refrigerator contained food that was no longer edible and she neglected to purchase fresh produce. She stopped going outside by herself, for she often forgot where she was going, and crossing the street frightened her. She lost her incentive to do things and was no longer motivated to keep up her appearance. She was suspicious of everyone and their motives, not trusting anyone and accusing all of wanting her clothes, her furniture, her food and her money. She became withdrawn and unpredictable.

By the time Annie was eighty-five, I was visiting her every day. But there were times it was an effort to cross the threshold of her apartment. What had once been a place of warmth and comfort had become a place of neglect and suspicion.

"Ma, where's the carpet cleaner?" I asked one day.

"Why?" she answered.

"Your apartment is dirty. There's a bad odour of rotting food," I replied, walking over to the storeroom to see if the carpet cleaner was still there. It was leaning against the back wall and I dragged it out to the centre of the room.

"What are you doing?" Annie shrieked.

"I'm going to clean the carpet," I said, pushing the brush over the crumbs of food that littered the floor.

Annie pushed herself from her chair and with unusual strength gripped my wrist, preventing me from continuing. "Stop!" she cried. "You're embarrassing me. This is not your work – this is mine. I will do it."

"Ma, you need help!"

"No! I can take care of myself."

"Ma, your clothes are not clean – let me take them home and clean them."

"No! I will clean them myself."

"Ma, you're losing weight. You don't eat."

"I eat when I'm hungry."

"Ma, let me put you in a nursing home, where you can get help."

"No! Never!"

I ARRANGED TO have a woman care for Annie eight hours a day. Her speech slowed and she didn't always finish a sentence. There were times when she didn't respond to her name and other times when she was her old self. Her health continued to deteriorate. My brothers and I had to make a decision. She had told me it was a gift to be in two places at once, but now Annie spent far too little time in the real world.

I STOOD BY the door peering at the dark silhouette of my mother in her bed, tears streamed down my cheeks. "Ma, I love you. I know you can't hear me," I said aloud, "but I hear you. I'll always hear you. Sweet dreams, Ma. You were right. It's never too late to dream."

Annie Abramovitz, aged ninety-two, passed away in her sleep on Thursday, December 1, 1994.

Few of us
ever achieve the acclaim of everyone,
but that is not to say fame has escaped us.

In the hearts of a handful of people
whose lives we have touched intimately,
our torch will continue to burn without us.

And who is to say
this is not a greater achievement,
to grasp fame without doing famous things,
to be loved for what we were
instead of what we were able to become,
to be forgiven our faults,
and to be celebrated simply for our spirit,
our character
and our willingness to try?

Anonymous

Section Two:

Stories of Mystery

Road Rage

THE OLD CAR sped down the highway at well over the speed limit; its occupants, a husband and his wife, sat in the front seat separated by more than the armrest. The woman in the passenger seat peered at a map, uncomplimentary words gushing from her mouth, while he gripped the wheel so tightly his knuckles were white. "Will you put that map down, Charlotte?" he said. "We're not lost. This highway will take us to Rochester."

"Why didn't you take the thruway like I told you?"

"Why didn't you drive if you wanted to go that way?"

"You're so goddamn stubborn," she said. "The thruway is easier to drive on. You deliberately took this way to antagonize me." Her face reddened as her anger mounted.

"It's shorter," he answered, raising his voice, "and the thruway costs money. Instead of going through Buffalo, we crossed the border at Lewiston because our motel is just south of Highway 104 in north Rochester and this is Highway 104. It'll take us straight to the motel providing the police don't arrest you for not wearing your seat belt."

"You're an idiot!"

"You always say that when you don't get your way. Can't you ever let things just be? We promised not to fight this weekend. I promised to come and you promised to stop being critical of everything I did."

"And you promised not to be critical of everything I did," she mimicked in a nasal imitation of him. "That's impossible. You go out of your way to screw things up."

He clenched his teeth not wanting to say something unpleasant. "Watch the signs," he said. "I can't focus on my driving and listen to your bleating. We have to make a dogleg turn soon without getting off this highway. If we don't, we'll be on another highway."

"We're late!" she said angrily.

"No, we're not. And when we get to the motel, I'm lying down. You can visit with your family. I put in a full day working yesterday – you didn't."

"You've become impossible to live with," she retorted. "You always have a stupid answer. A little humility wouldn't hurt you."

He ground his teeth and forced himself not to reply. She never saw his side. She had become selfish over the years. All she did was put him down. His mouth curled, but he fought back the ugly words that were on the tip of his tongue.

"Watch where you're driving," she bleated, interrupting his thoughts. "This stupid map was made upside down and nothing makes sense."

"I don't need the map." His tone held more than a trace of sarcasm. He glanced at his wife. They had been married almost twenty years and she'd been nagging for the last ten. Her mouth was always moving, always spewing vitriol directed at him. How he wished he could tune her out. He tried to focus his attention on his driving, but his mind churned with images of him inflicting pain on her. Her voice filtered through his thoughts as she continued her harangue about the thruway, her sister being married for the third time, life being a bitch, their neighbours having everything and she having nothing and on and on. There never appeared an end to her misery. God, how he hated her! How he hated the direction his life had taken. He struggled through his boring life, accepting each day, knowing that it would not get any better – in fact, aware it would get worse.

"Yes, dear," he said, just to give the impression he had been listening. His foot had unconsciously pressed harder on the accelerator and the car picked up speed.

"I know what you're doing," Charlotte said, turning to him. "You think by driving fast you can prove to me that this way is shorter than mine. I'm not stupid. Are you trying to get us killed? Slow this car down immediately. We're going to be late and it's your fault. You never do anything right . . ." The complaints poured forth.

"I'll kill her," he muttered under his breath. Why wouldn't she just stop complaining? What does she want from me? I work hard. I've never cheated on her. So I'm not a social animal. I'm too tired after work to go out for an evening of social togetherness. "Take me here. Take me there. You're not romantic." Why couldn't she appreciate him for himself? Be grateful that he never fooled around? If he fell asleep watching television, she called him lazy. If he dropped food on the floor while he was eating, she said he was a slob. And sex . . . it was virtually non-existent between them now. She complained he was too rough, too heavy and too demanding. Too demanding! That's a joke. He was lucky if he got it even once a month. And when he did, doing it was nearly impossible, her being so big that it was a struggle to get close enough to make penetration.

"Where are we?" Charlotte bellowed. "Why haven't we come to Rochester? Are we lost?"

"How can we be lost? This highway only goes to Rochester," he shouted back.

"Did you make the turn? I don't remember you making the turn. I bet you didn't. This is not the right road. We aren't going to Rochester. We're going to be really late. I knew it, I knew it."

His stomach was tied in knots. He'd been lost in his thoughts and hadn't paid attention to the road. He looked for a highway sign, but none appeared. Then he saw an expanse of blue on the horizon. Lake Ontario? Damn. That wasn't right. He must have turned, but the wrong way. No wonder, driving with her. The continuous harangue was enough to make anyone lose their way. He tried to figure out where they were heading from the direction of the setting sun.

"Pull over at the next gas station!" she demanded.

"There aren't any."

"Don't get smart with me. You really got us lost. You never do anything right."

It was then he decided he would kill her – but how?

"We aren't lost," he said coldly. "I made the wrong turn and we're headed for Lake Ontario."

"What? Stop this car and turn around. Do you hear me, pull over!"

He pulled over to the shoulder of the highway and stopped. He buried his head between his arms still resting on the wheel, his head pounding from her incessant nagging.

"Don't try to make like you're sick. I'm the one who's sick. I'm the one who should be barfing all over the road. If I wasn't strong, that's what I'd be doing. You're impossible. Get out! Get out! I'm driving. That's the last time I let you drive me to my sister's. The last!"

He groped for the handle and pushed the door open. The occasional car whizzed by and he was tempted, so tempted, to push her in front of one. Push her in front of one and watch her bounce. He grinned at the image.

"Is that a smirk on your face?" she demanded. "How dare you

laugh at me after the stupid thing you've done. We're miles from where we should be and you think that's funny?"

She tried to slide behind the steering wheel, but her bulk wouldn't allow it. She groped for the lever to push the seat back, then heaved herself in. "How can you drive so close to the wheel? What's the matter with you?" She settled herself into a comfortable position as he buckled himself into the passenger seat. She stepped on the accelerator, jerking the car back onto the highway. U-turning without signalling, she caused an oncoming car to veer sharply onto the gravel to avoid hitting her, while she sped away in the opposite direction.

"Stupid driver," she complained as she heard the repeated sound of honking from the car she'd forced off the road. "That idiot could tell I was going to go the other way. He did that deliberately." Charlotte hunched forward and pressed her foot harder on the accelerator, making the car speed back over the highway, faster than the speed limit.

He closed his eyes in the hope he could remove the sound of her. He hated her. More than hate, it was revulsion. It was hard to believe that once, many years ago, she had been beautiful. Once, when they were first married, he had worshipped her. But that was then.

"Are you sleeping?" she snapped. "I don't believe this. I'm forced to drive and you go to sleep. It's so typical of you. You deliberately went out of your way because you don't like my sister. I know what you did. I'm not stupid. You never wanted to come in the first place. This was your way of getting even. You're so small-minded . . ."

His fingers curled into a fist.

"Where are we?" she demanded. "Do you hear me? Open your goddamn eyes and tell me where we are."

He opened his eyes and glared at her. The sun was almost on the horizon. Darkness was speeding towards them. "You're going too fast," he said. "Slow down."

"I am not going too fast. I know how to drive. Whoever posted these speed limits was a moron. Where are we? Am I coming to the cut off?"

He peered at the signs flashing past and tried to read them. A large billboard appeared, but at their speed, he was only able to catch the first line. "It's time to change your life." He shifted his eyes to his wife and mentally threw a knife at her. He could envision the surprise on her face, the strangling sound she would make. He imagined her choking on her own blood.

"What are you staring at?" she snarled.

He turned his head and faced the front. The anger in him boiled.

Suddenly, she pulled onto the narrow gravel shoulder, the soft earth throwing a cloud of dust behind them as she braked abruptly. She opened her door and climbed out. He watched as she walked back to look at a sign still obscured by the flying dust bowl she had created. She had left the car running. The humming of the engine was all he could hear; it was a blessing. He placed his hand on the gearshift. All he had to do was pull it into reverse. One pull and the car would back over her and her mouth would stop forever.

Initially he had felt responsible for what had happened to his marriage. She said he drove her to distraction because he was dull. Was he always dull? If so, what was it she saw in him when they were first married? Had he changed so much? He didn't know. He knew she had had an affair, but he didn't want her to know he knew. He didn't know who the lover was or how long the affair had lasted, but one day the lover was gone. There was no warning. He didn't have to be a rocket scientist to figure out that something bad had happened to her. He'd overheard her on the telephone pleading to the empty receiver, begging for her lover to answer. Her bitterness at being rejected had changed her, made a lovely young woman into an angry shrew.

There was a pounding on the car. She was gesturing for him to come out. He looked down at his hand on the gearshift lever and reluctantly released his hold. He opened his door and walked around to where she stood.

"Look! Look!" she demanded, pointing to the sign.

He turned to stare at the sign and tried not to smile. It read 'Highway 490. Five Miles. Keep Right.' They had passed the turn again and were almost at the thruway.

Her huge bulk jiggled as she bumped him aside with her body and entered the passenger side of the car. He wished he had a gun. He would stick it in her mouth and empty all the bullets into that cavern of obscenity. The look in her eyes at the moment of impact would be his reward. And just before her head disintegrated, he would shout at her, "Why didn't you tell me? I would have understood. I know I wasn't blameless."

Now, he didn't care. Now, he just wanted her to stop talking. He decided he would buy a gun.

She glared at him from behind the windshield and honked the horn. He got into the driver's side and brought the seat forward. He glanced behind him to see if there was any traffic and then moved the car into the lane, heading for the entrance to the thruway that would take them to the south of Rochester. Her mouth was going again. He wished he had a knife; forget about the gun. If he had a knife he would stick it into her and watch all the air fart out, reducing her to a third her size. He kept glancing at her, his focus on her mouth, opening and closing, and not his driving. He heard her raise her voice, but was too engrossed in his fantasy of putting an end to her life. He didn't hear her words or notice the detour barrier directing cars to a temporary entrance to Highway 490. His foot weighed a ton and he wasn't aware how fast the car was travelling. He didn't feel the impact when the car struck the inner part of the concrete barrier.

Smoke poured from under the car. The passenger door was open; Charlotte had been thrown clear of the vehicle onto the thick lush grass. She truly had bounced when she hit the soft ground. Her arms and legs were lacerated and there was a slow flow of blood from her nose. She struggled to her feet and stormed over to the wrecked vehicle. The hood jutted straight up and the driver's side of the vehicle had buckled like an accordion. Her mouth opened and closed as her words gushed out. He looked at her from inside the car through half closed eyes. He saw her mouth moving but no sound penetrated his ears. He smiled as his eyes closed. He wasn't coming out, no matter what she said. The steering column had collapsed and a section had penetrated his chest.

He no longer heard her.

He no longer cared.

He had shut her out for good.

The
Credit Card
Caper

HE WAS SEETHING. David Cooper looked at his watch for the tenth time. He had come home early to rest, business was stagnant, his cash flow at the moment stank, and his frustration was affecting his breathing. When he opened his mail, he was confronted by yet another problem. His wife, Beverley, had promised not to use her credit card until their finances improved, but she had broken her word. Again.

He was a retired cop on a half-yearly pension, selling security alarm systems in partnership with his brother-in-law. They were not in bad financial shape, but business was down right now and so was his pay. Once more, he glanced at the bank statement lying on the kitchen table. "Damn it, Beverley, you promised!" he almost shouted out loud. "You promised you wouldn't do this again. A bargain is no bargain if we don't have the money to pay for the damn thing." This time he was going to ask for her card back. If she couldn't cut her spending, then he'd take the credit card away from her.

He didn't need this tension. Quitting the police force because of a heart attack was hard enough. Scrimping was humiliating. Fighting with Beverley was not something he enjoyed. If it wasn't for her, he could be dead. He had come home in the middle of the day about a year ago and told her he thought he had indigestion and was going to lie down. But she thought otherwise and made him go to the hospital. He owed her. But, damn, they were in a financial pinch and she knew it. They didn't need another television, certainly not one with a 34-inch screen.

He heard the front door open. Beverley smiled when she saw him and came over to give him a kiss. "Hi, hon," she said. Seeing the hard look in his eyes, she paused. "Something the matter? You okay?"

David moved his head towards the kitchen table, focusing his gaze on the single sheet of paper. "You promised," he said.

Beverley picked up the statement and read it. "I didn't make this purchase. Why would I buy a television?"

"You didn't buy a TV?"

"No, I didn't. What for?"

"Well, if you didn't, who did? That's our statement." David gritted his teeth when he realized he had accused his wife wrongly. He shook his head to clear the anger. "Jeez. I'm sorry," he said weakly. "I've been fuming ever since I saw the statement because I thought . . . I'm sorry, dear. I've had a bad day and the statement just capped it off. I wasn't thinking." He looked uncomfortable. "I'm sorry. How about giving me that kiss?" he said, trying to smile through his embarrassment. "We'll start fresh."

"Nope." Beverley said. "Penalty for not having faith in me." But she smiled. Beverley examined the statement. "Today, when I went to use the credit card to pay for the groceries, I had to pay in cash because the expiry date was last week and I hadn't noticed." She rummaged in her purse and brought out her credit card. "Look. See."

David took her card and examined the date. "You should have received your renewal a few weeks ago. Damn! Now I am mad. Some son of a bitch is using our card. You had better notify the bank right away."

Beverley gasped and went to the telephone.

THREE WEEKS LATER, David Cooper came home at the end of the day, looking tired. Beverley came to him as he hung up his coat. "Where have you been?"

"What do you mean, where have I been?"

"Don't play games with me. Where have you been and don't make like I'm stupid?"

"Business."

"Monkey business."

"Business."

"Bull! You're snooping."

"Who says?"

"My brother. I called to see how you were and he hummed and hawed when I asked to speak to you. When he starts sounding like a jackass, I know he's covering something up. So, where were you? Snooping?"

"Beverley, don't bury me. I had a heart attack. I'm better. It's my heart that was damaged, not my brain."

"You're so stubborn. You almost died. When I wanted you to go to the hospital, you said no. You could hardly breathe. Do you want to die? You're off the force because there's a risk to your life. A high risk. You don't need tension." Her anger waned and her face softened. "I don't want you to die. I don't." She looked at him, her eyes pleading. "Forget about the television."

David reached into his coat pocket and brought out a small pad. "I got my list of suspects down to six people."

"You promised, David. You said no more snooping after you retired."

"This is different."

"No, this is an excuse. Can't you get being a cop out of your system?"

David's face broke into a sheepish grin. "It's not easy, Beverley. It stirs the blood. It's an adrenaline surge unlike anything else when you're closing in on the suspect. I hated having to retire. You know that. Give me some slack. I can solve this case. My friends at the precinct are too busy chasing serious crooks to worry about this penny ante credit card thief."

"Penny ante! Not if he'd gotten the right card with a higher credit limit."

"Maybe."

"What do you mean, maybe?"

David flipped several pages. "It's been three weeks since we got our statement and almost five since the purchase of the television. He made only one purchase on our card. He's selective. Normally, credit card thieves make several quick purchases before ditching the card. He made only one. It was deliberate."

"How do you know? All you know is that he hit us for a 34-inch television. He could be using other cards big time. And besides, why a he and not a she?"

"Answer to question one, my gut says I'm right. As for question two, I went to the appliance store where the television was purchased to see if the sales clerk might remember the buyer. All the clerk could recall was that he wore a hat and tinted glasses. Apparently, he walked into the store on Saturday when there was a lot of action, gave the model of the television and offered our card. He was asked for I.D. and he produced a letter addressed to me from the policeman's association. He had my mail. I checked with the association and they said a letter was sent to me notifying me of a meeting. When the purchase was cleared, he said he was bringing his car around the back to take the television with him. An employee helped him put it into a blue van, but couldn't remember the licence and only recalls the guy gave him a two dollar tip. In, out and gone in less than twenty-five minutes. Planned and executed without a hitch."

"All right, he's smart. Why are you getting involved? We're not paying for the television."

"You're right, we're not. But this guy used our credit card and stole our mail. I'm pissed off. Besides, he's not smart. I'm almost sure who it was."

"You listen to me, David Cooper. You're overweight, out of shape and your heart is giving you trouble. I want you to stop."

"I'll be careful," David said.

"No, you won't. Stop! Do not get me pissed off, as you aptly put it. I'll become your worse daymare."

"Yes, dear."

"IT'S OUR MAILMAN," David told his brother-in-law, George as they were having a coffee.

"Why him?"

"Credit cards are mailed. That made him a suspect. Using my mail to identify himself leads me to the same deduction."

"It could have been someone from the bank," George said. "It could have been someone from the post office sorting room. It could have been one or two of your neighbours. The Raskins or the Thompsons. Either one is capable of doing something like this. Someone could have taken it from your mailbox. Your mail sits outside all day until someone comes home."

"I actually thought about my neighbours. You're right, those two walk a thin line in stock brokering, but it's not their expertise. They carry big sticks, but they haven't got the brains to use them. Besides, they both make more money than I do."

"It could have been a stranger."

"True. It could have been anyone, even you, but let's use our heads. It's too risky for a stranger to walk over to a mailbox next to a front door and remove mail without the risk of someone seeing him. Not practical. It's a matter of elimination. The renewal card never reached us. Between the time it was being sent to us and when we should have received it, it was diverted. The bank is satisfied it's not someone working for them. Internal security checked out the department responsible for the cards and I see no reason to doubt them. They say there haven't been any other cases of credit card hijacking in their branch until this series. And it stopped almost as soon as it began. That I found interesting."

"What series? Are you saying you weren't the only one whose card was stolen?"

"Nope. Four credit cards were stolen over a two-week period with only one purchase from each card. That in itself is strange. And the owners of the cards don't all use the same branch. That ruled out a local bank employee because that would have had to be a conspiracy with an employee at every branch. Too complicated. What I have is four cards and the same M.O. The only problem is my mailman doesn't own a blue van. I checked."

"You're a real Sherlock Holmes, hey! Weren't you supposed to back off? Beverley told me she gave you an ultimatum."

"Don't tell her what I'm doing. I can solve this – and soon."

"You know you'll get me into trouble with my sister. She's a terror when she's mad and I'm not interested in having her on me. I'll make you a deal, David. I'll cover for you for one more week. I know my sister. She'll be watching to see if you change your work habits. She's not stupid. One week. No more."

"I promise. One week."

"So tell me, this mailman of yours, do you know him?"

"No. I don't think I've ever seen him. The superintendent at the post office cooperated with me after I explained that I was a detective until I retired and someone there remembered me from a previous case. They gave me a list of mailmen in my area and I ran a check on them through the precinct's computer. Three of them had habits. Bad habits: Gambling, prescription drugs and alcohol. One wasn't in the city on the day of the big purchase, away in Atlantic City for the weekend. One was in the hospital for elective surgery and the other had a good alibi. He was in jail for the weekend sleeping it off. With them most likely all cleared, I focused on my mailman. I hit pay dirt there."

"What?"

"Empty corrugated cartons in front of his house indicated recent large item purchases. There was a discarded old appliance in the lane behind his house and one neighbour said he recently bought a 34-inch television. I asked about his sudden wealth and a couple of his neighbours said he'd won a lottery."

"Did he?"

"Yes."

"So why him?"

"The earliest credit card misuse was two weeks before he won the money. My television was the last item he bought. That night he became a winner."

"Can you prove it?"

"Not unless I can get into his house and identify the items. I can't get a search warrant on what I have."

"What are you going to do?"

"Keep investigating."

DAVID ENTERED HIS office and threw himself into his chair. George came in, saw the look on his face and took a seat opposite him. "You look like you're about to burst."

"The son-of-a-gun's got me running in circles. This guy's smoother than I thought," David said.

"Still think it's the mailman?"

"Positive. The purchases stopped because the mailman won a ton of money. He got lucky, not smarter. He quit his job. He's retired. Crime pays if you're lucky."

"Is that envy, David?"

"I hate losing a case."

"This is not a case."

"Yes, it is. I made it my case."

"Listen, hotshot," George said, smiling, "you ain't on a case. You are retired, remember?"

"I never quit on any of my caseloads when I was on the force and I'm not starting now. I made this my case and I'm going to solve it."

"Even if he's caught, he'll only be given a suspended sentence. The courts are too clogged with real cases. They'll plea-bargain him and make him return the money. He's got it. Big deal. Why put yourself into a lather?"

"I screwed up, George. I'm mad at myself for accusing Beverley and I'm mad at him for putting the thought in my head. He's going down."

George shook his head. "Tomorrow is your last day. Remember, you promised – and no reprieve."

A MIDDLE-AGED MAN answered his knock at the door. "Mr. Holt," David began, "my name is David Cooper. I would like to talk to you about credit cards. May I come in?"

"I have several credit cards," Mr. Holt answered.

"I know. I'm referring to other peoples. Mine in particular."

Timothy Holt smiled and stepped back, opening the door wider to allow David to enter. They were in the living room where Holt's wife and two teenagers were watching a program on a 34-inch television. There was the smell of new renovations, the furniture had an unused look and the carpet looked too clean to have been there long.

"Somewhere private, Mr. Holt."

Timothy Holt continued into the kitchen and sat on a chair. David remained standing. He glanced around. Everything appeared sparkling new. The cupboards had been replaced and the floor had been recently laid. "What was it that you were referring to?" Holt said.

"That's my television," David said, pointing towards the other room.

"It's mine," Timothy answered, "I bought it."

"I know. With my credit card."

Timothy grinned. "Really?"

Mrs. Holt entered the kitchen.

"Hello," she said. "I'm sorry we chased you into the kitchen. That television is addictive. The screen's so big. It's like being at the movies." She moved to stand by her husband and put her hands on his shoulder. "Can I get you something to drink?" she asked.

"No, thanks. I won't be long. I'm updating the realty records," David said, not wanting to make any statements that might cause a scene.

"Have we ever met?"

"Uh, no, Mrs. Holt," David replied. "I don't live in this area."

"Are you sure I can't get you something to drink?"

"No thank you," David said, his eyes on Timothy Holt's smirking face.

"Actually, dear," Holt said, "he was admiring our new television."

"Would you like to watch it?"

"No, thanks. No. It's a beautiful piece of furniture. Must be expensive."

"It would have been," she said, "but we got lucky. My lottery pool at the office came though and I shared in a lot of money. Well, I'll leave the two of you alone. Nice to have met you, Mr. . . ."

"Cooper."

"Mr. Cooper." She hurriedly left the kitchen.

Timothy Holt had a long grin that almost left his face.

David faced him angrily. "I've figured you out, Mr. Holt. I've tracked your moves. I know the stores you went to and the items you bought. If you let me, I'm sure I'll find each item in your house."

"Not anymore."

"The television?"

Timothy Holt shrugged. "Why are you telling me this? Looking for a confession?" He stared at David, curiosity on his face. "No, I don't think so. Something else?"

"To let you know I know."

"I'm glad you do. I'm glad someone does. But the knowing isn't going to help you. You look like a person who has a lot. Do you know what it's like to work all your life and have nothing? I do. I bring mail to people who don't know me, who live in houses I could never afford and I ask myself why. I decided not to ask anymore, Mr. Cooper. And I also got lucky." Timothy stood. "It's a pleasure meeting you, Mr. Cooper. You live in a nice house. I'll think of you every time I watch television." He paused as David glared at him. "What do you do for a living, Mr. Cooper, sit behind a desk?"

"No, Mr. Holt. I was a cop – robbery."

Mr. Holt smiled broadly. "All the better." He walked to the front door and opened it. As David passed him, he said, "Have a nice day."

MEETING WITH TIMOTHY Holt had been a defiant gesture. His deadline was up. It wasn't the deadline that stopped him; his work got busy and he found himself immersed in sales. A couple of times, he went to the local precinct and asked the desk sergeant if there was anything new on the case. He found out there wasn't even a detective assigned. He told the superintendent his suspicions, but apparently their caseload was too heavy to find time for something that was no longer active.

He was having trouble walking away.

He went back to the electronic store to find out if they kept serial numbers of the items they sold. They did. Now what he needed to do was match the numbers in their possession with the one on Timothy Holt's television. The trick was how to get into the Holt house and find out. The blue van was another problem. If the man didn't own one, did he rent one or borrow it from someone, and if he borrowed it, then from whom? These were the questions he couldn't answer.

"You're still fooling around, aren't you?" George asked.

"Not much time for that, but yes, I'm still trying to get a handle on it."

"Beverley's suspicious. She calls a few times every day, asking about you."

"I haven't been on it this week. I've been too busy. You of all people should know that."

"I told her, but I don't think she believes me."

"You know, if I had a search warrant, I would get him. I just need to see the television set close up."

"So, get one."

"I don't have probable cause. You can't just go into a house on a hunch. Besides, I have no status. If I knew who he knew that owned a blue van, I'd have something."

"Let it pass, David. It sounds like you're going in circles."

David nodded.

A WEEK LATER, George entered David's office with a newspaper. "Thought you would be interested in an item on page four," he said, handing David the open page.

WINNER LOSES

Bad luck came to Timothy Holt, husband of one of the winners of the Super Lottery three months ago. He was struck on the expressway while changing a tire of a borrowed van and was run over by a passing mail truck. According to his wife, he was taking their television to be repaired. She said he had bought the television from their winnings, but couldn't find the sales slip and the store didn't have a record of the purchase. He decided to take the television to a repair shop that specializes in large sets when the accident occurred. He had recently retired. His foreman commended him for his dedication, always being on his route no matter the weather.

"I saw it earlier," David said.

"You don't look pleased."

"That's a high price to pay for a television set."

"No, it's not. That's justice."

"No, it's stupidity."

"How's that?"

"Two weeks after he stole his first item, they won the lottery. He ditched everything he stole except the television. He could have bought another damn television instead of trying to have it fixed. He was clever, but there are times when smart people do stupid things for the wrong reasons. His old habits were hard to break. He was too used to pinching his pennies. He beat me but he didn't beat the system."

"Did you tell Beverley the case was solved?"

"Yeah. She said to take notice of what happens when you cheat. I think that was a warning." He laughed. "I think she's telling me I'd better stay away from this stuff."

"Will you?"

"No."

A Story In Two Words

"COME ON, MY good man, open it! Open it, I say! What! What! You agreed to the rules. We fed you, now it's time to pay the piper. Don't take all day. What does it say?"

Dr. Jon Podgorska wondered why he had agreed to participate in this insane evening. His host was a pompous ass; a rich man living a life of boredom and uselessness, getting his kicks listening to someone else's experiences. Well, he was committed. He'd come to the rich man's private club and he had to admit the food was good; better than the food he would have ordered in the tavern near his boarding house.

The truth was, he'd come because he was bored. He was a medical pensioner who had assisted the allies during the war and was now living alone in a foreign country. He had few friends and too much time on his hands. When the rich man had invited him for a New Year's Eve supper, he had accepted, more for the companionship than anything else. The price for the supper, though, was ridiculous. It seemed that every New Year's, an outsider was invited to dinner to tell the members a true story the subject of which was determined by a random selection from sealed envelopes, each containing two words. The story had to be crafted from the two words.

The twenty men in the room made themselves comfortable on high-backed, overstuffed chairs. Some smoked cigars, a few lit pipes. All were over sixty-five, relics of an era long past. Podgorska went to a table and selected an envelope. He tore the short side open.

"Well, what's it say, man? Can you tell a story or can't you?"

Podgorska shook the envelope and a small card slipped out. He studied the words and cast his thoughts back, trying to come up with a story to comply with their silly rules.

"Bless my soul, I've never seen the like. Are you asleep? What! What! Get on with it."

Podgorska bit down on his lip. He wanted to answer back but he controlled his anger and began his story. "The place is Poland. The year, I believe was 1921. The city was Lodz. A young man, whom I will call Solomon Lefkovitz . . ."

SOLOMON WAS MESMERIZED by the philosophy of Russia's 1917 Bolshevik Revolution and became a dedicated Communist at a time when Communism was illegal in Poland. An angry man, and outspoken, he condemned the corruption in the government and so offended many with his biting criticism that, finally, several prominent politicians threatened him. These threats he discounted as rhetoric without merit.

On this particular November day, he had been at Gershon Weinberg's printing shop, where he and his overweight friend published a newspaper. He had left early to check on the condition of his wife, Miriam, who was due to give birth any day. When he arrived home he noticed that the front door to his apartment building was slightly ajar. He hurried up the steps, unaware of Mrs. Tanenbaum and Mrs. Shapiro staring at him from the doorway of their building across the court or of the faces behind the windows gazing down into the courtyard.

He entered his apartment and called out, "Miriam. I'm home."

His greeting was met with silence.

He knew she was home. The last couple of days she hadn't left the apartment because climbing the stairs tired her so. Solomon tensed. It was not like her to leave the apartment without telling him.

He called again as he hurried through the living room to the bedroom. "Miriam!"

No response.

He was seized by the fear that she might be lying helpless on the floor. A few times Miriam had admitted she was dizzy. The bed was rumpled, but the room was empty.

Solomon called again. "Miriam!"

Still no answer.

He glanced about, hoping to see a note.

Nothing.

He entered the kitchen.

Something was wrong. A chair lay on its side and the table was out of place. On the floor, under the chair, he noticed a large pool of dark red. His heart pounded. He bent down and ran his finger through it. It was blood. Had his preoccupation with his political cause and his overconfidence endangered the one person he cherished more than life itself?

He raced down the stairs, but before he reached the bottom, the front door burst open. Gershon charged through, his face flushed.

"Miriam's been taken to Radergosht Hospital!" he wheezed.

Solomon didn't wait to hear another word. He bolted past Gershon, out the door and raced through the streets to the hospital. Gershon had warned him to stay home with Miriam and his words now swept through Solomon's thoughts as he tore past the strolling pedestrian traffic. He crossed the intersection against traffic and barely avoided being run over by the horse-drawn vehicles. His cap had blown off and his hair blew wildly in the wind. People stopped to watch his frantic flight, aware that something terrible must have happened.

He barged through the emergency door of the hospital, his breathing laboured. Frantically, he rushed towards a nun standing behind the reception counter. "Where's my wife? Where did they take her?" he asked loudly, an edge of panic and hysteria in his voice.

Startled, the nun asked, "What is your wife's name?"

"Miriam Lefkovitz. My friend said she was here. I found blood on the floor in our apartment. She wasn't expected to give birth until next week. Something must have happened. Where is she?"

The nun paled. "Please wait here. I'll get Dr. Golom." She hurried down the hall and passed through another set of doors.

Solomon paced the reception area like a lion in a cage. The antiseptic odours filled his nostrils and caused bile to rise in his throat. As he prowled the floor, he never took his eyes from the door the nun had gone through.

Then the door to the outside crashed open and Gershon rushed in. "Did you find her?" he gasped.

"No. The nun went to get the doctor."

Gershon staggered to a chair and collapsed onto it, causing the wood joints to protest. "Who's the doctor?" he asked, handing Solomon his hat.

"A Dr. Golom."

"Shit! I know him. He's a stickler for rules. He's so straight and narrow you can't talk to him. He demands things his way. A real *putz*. He and I have had words."

"I don't care about him. How did you know Miriam was here?"

Gershon's hand disappeared into his pocket and he pulled out his handkerchief. "Shlomo came to the shop after you left. He saw an ambulance leaving your courtyard and asked Mrs. Tanenbaum what happened." Gershon wiped his eyes and took a swipe at his nose. "Mrs. Tanenbaum said she saw two men running from your building. When she went to investigate, she found Miriam lying on the floor." Gershon paused and averted his eyes.

"Go on! What else?"

"Miriam was covered in blood," Gershon added reluctantly.

Solomon uttered a low moan and covered his eyes.

"Mrs. Tanenbaum ran down the stairs screaming. Mrs. Shapiro heard her and ran out into the street to look for help." Gershon stood and returned his soiled handkerchief to his pocket. "She was unconscious when they brought her downstairs." He placed his hand on Solomon's shoulder.

Solomon flung it off and glared at him.

"I'm surprised you and Shlomo didn't meet in the street on your way home."

Solomon's eyes filled with tears. "I stopped at the bakery. It was so busy, I left without buying anything." He stared at the door as if willing the nun to return. And just then the door did open and the nun hurried towards them. Before she had a chance to speak, Solomon was upon her, "My wife, where is she? Is she all right?" Towering over her, Solomon demanded, "Take me to my wife."

"The doctor is treating . . ."

The door opened again and a short, middle-aged man emerged. He was almost bald, his wire-rimmed glasses sat precariously on the tip of his nose and the white smock he wore was stained with blood.

He crossed over to Solomon and was about to speak when Solomon again demanded, "I want to see my wife. Where is she?"

"Mr. Lefkovitz? I am Dr. Moses Golom."

"Where's my wife?" Solomon asked again.

"Could you come with me to my office? I will explain everything there."

"No!"

Taken aback by Solomon's rudeness, Dr. Golom said, "Mr. Lefkovitz, I don't think you understand. There are procedures to follow."

"I don't care. I want to see my wife." Solomon clenched his fists in anger.

"Sir, please. Come to my office. This is a matter of some privacy."

Solomon glared at the doctor and didn't move.

Dr. Golom sighed "Your wife had an accident . . ."

Solomon paled. He teetered momentarily from the impact of the doctor's implications, then impatiently pushed Dr. Golom aside and entered the door through which he had come. It opened onto a narrow passageway flanked by curtained cubicles, each lit by a single light bulb.

A nurse appeared from one enclosure. "Sir, you are not allowed..."

Dr. Golom caught up with him, his face red with anger. "Sir, you can't come in here!" he said furiously. "This is a treatment ward! You are not allowed. I insist you leave immediately. Come to my office and I will explain about your wife."

Again Solomon shoved Dr. Golom aside. He pulled back the curtain of the nearest cubicle. It was empty. He pulled back the curtain of the next, and then the next.

"Miriam! Miriam!" he shouted. He pulled back another curtain. An old woman lay on a bed, holding a bloody cloth to her chin. One arm was taped to two pieces of wood. Her face was ashen with pain.

"Leave, or I'll call the police!" Golom shouted.

Solomon charged back to the doctor. "Damn you! Where is she?"

"I will not answer until you leave this area. I am a doctor. Have you no respect for my position? I will not be treated in this manner and I expect a full apology for your behaviour."

Solomon grabbed the short man by his neck and thrust his face into his. "You son of a bitch! Where is she?"

The nurse ran through the doorway to the reception area.

Golom, choking for breath, his eyes bulging, his face turning red, grabbed at Solomon's hand, trying to pry it from his throat.

Suddenly Gershon was at Solomon's side. "Let him go, Solomon!" he shouted. "Let him go!"

Solomon relaxed his grip and Dr. Golom collapsed to the floor, gasping and clutching at his throat.

Gershon dropped to his knees and leaned into Dr. Golom's face. "For your own sake, sir, tell my friend where he can find his wife."

The doctor took a few seconds to regain his composure. "How dare he treat me this way!" he sputtered.

Gershon slapped him hard across the face, leaving a reddened imprint of his hand on the doctor's cheek. "Tell my friend where he can find his wife," Gershon repeated, his voice hardened.

"Room 310," the doctor muttered.

Gershon turned to Solomon and realized he was gone. He rushed out to the reception, then to the stairs. Taking them two at a time, he ploughed into people moving more slowly, emerging at last onto the third floor. He saw Solomon just ahead. He forced his heavy body into a sprint and narrowed the gap between them. A light bulb over the door flickered and died, leaving the hallway gray and foreboding. Both men stared at the dead bulb.

Solomon turned to Gershon, his face drawn, eyes pleading. "Gershon, I'm afraid," he whispered.

Gershon gently placed a hand on his friend's shoulder. "We'll go in together." But Solomon closed his eyes and remained fixed in place, perspiration glistening on his skin. Gershon entered the open doorway to the ward. The room was shrouded in semi-darkness. There were eight occupied beds, but only one had a portable partition around it. Solomon stepped forward; Gershon remained by the entrance.

"Miriam," Solomon whispered, "Miriam!" his voice louder, her name a wail. "Please . . . No!" Solomon pulled away the partition and fell to his knees by the bed, his hand clutching at the sheet. "Don't do this," he pleaded. "It's not fair!" he cried, burying his head into the side of the bed, sobbing uncontrollably.

Gershon pressed his head hard against the doorjamb.

Solomon had drawn back the sheet covering the body to reveal Miriam's bandaged head; she appeared to be asleep. He held her hand and, between sobs, pleaded with her to awaken. Unable to watch any longer, Gershon backed out of the room.

A nun approached. "Sir." Her voice was strained. "We're so sorry about the woman. It was fortunate Dr. Golom was here. No one else could have saved the baby."

Gershon's face showed confusion. "The baby?"

"The woman's baby. The doctor was able to save the baby before she died."

"My God!" He'd forgotten about the baby. "That bastard! Why didn't he tell us he'd saved the baby?"

"Sir?"

"My friend doesn't know their child is alive. Right now there's a lot of anger in him against the doctor. Tell Golom to lock himself in his office until I can tell my friend about the baby and calm him down."

The nun fled.

Gershon paced the hall. He could hear frantic voices at the nurses' station but was unable to understand what was being said. A nun quickly ran from the station and raced down the stairs.

"NOT TOO LONG afterwards, I appeared." Dr. Podgorska told his intent listeners. "Dr. Golom had made me aware of what had happened and I went immediately to the third floor. My first priority had been to talk to the nun at the nurses' section. She related her conversation with the huge man to me and I became extremely concerned as I pieced together what must have happened. As I stood at the desk, I could feel the large man watching me. I knew that I had to talk to someone, calmly, about what had happened before it mushroomed into something uncontrollable. I took the Lefkovitz folder from the nurse and I approached the man."

"I am Dr. Jon Podgorska, the physician-surgeon in charge." I extended my hand.

The giant man stared at me, not sure if he wanted to acknowledge another doctor. Reluctantly he shook my hand.

"Your name is . . .?" I asked.

"Gershon Weinberg."

"May I ask what your relationship is to the husband of the deceased?"

"Friend. Good friend."

"Do you think your friend is in a frame of mind to listen to what happened?"

Gershon shook his head.

"Dr. Golom has called the police," I said. "They are here now. He intends to lay charges against the two of you for assaulting him."

Gershon shook his head. "He refused to tell my friend where his wife was – my friend was frantic with fear. You had to be there to understand what happened."

"I understand the chain of events. I was made aware of what happened by Dr. Golom and the nun at the reception desk. Dr. Golom is an exceptional surgeon – his hands have performed miracles in our operating rooms – but he is a stickler for procedure."

"He's a bastard!" Gershon exclaimed.

I offered a weak smile. "He has no equal in this hospital when it comes to surgery. In fact, he'll be leaving us shortly and going to Warsaw."

Gershon made no reply.

"Would you come with me to the waiting room so I can explain to you what happened? The corridor is too public."

Gershon stared back at me without answering.

"The room is empty."

Gershon nodded.

I led the way into the waiting room. We sat. "I am not privy to what caused Mrs. Lefkovitz's injuries. All I can tell you is what happened to her from the time she was brought here. Do you understand?"

"Yes," Gershon responded.

I opened the folder. "Mrs. Lefkovitz arrived at the hospital by ambulance at 12:20 p.m." I glanced at the sheet. "The ambulance attendant informed Dr. Mikolajczyk in the emergency ward that he believed she had been assaulted. She was found on the floor of her apartment by a neighbour. She was bleeding from the head and hemorrhaging . . . between her legs."

Gershon clenched his fist so hard his knuckles turned white.

"Our examination revealed a severe contusion on her abdomen, caused by a blunt object, which resulted in internal bleeding. Also, a blow to her forehead caused a fracture of the skull and a considerable loss of blood. Her vital signs were at a dangerously low level when she arrived. Mrs. Lefkovitz was petite, rather delicate, and the blows were severe."

Gershon jumped to his feet, knocking over his chair. "She was nine months pregnant!" he exclaimed. "What animal could do such a thing?"

I nodded in sympathy. "Dr. Golom had two options and he had to make a decision quickly." I paused for Gershon to absorb my words. "Try to save the baby, lose the mother. Try to save the mother, lose the baby. Do you understand?"

"Why couldn't he save both?" Gershon asked.

"The possibility of saving the baby was excellent. Sadly, though, with Mrs. Lefkovitz's injuries, the chances of saving her were not favourable. Dr. Golom could have lost them both while trying to save the woman. His only real choice was to save the baby."

Gershon shook his head as if the gesture could untangle the shock of my words.

"If it had been me," I added, "I would have made the same decision. . . . And there is something else that you must understand. This is a Roman Catholic hospital and there are strict guidelines that apply in situations such as this. These matters are not decided flippantly, but by the teachings of the Church. Dr. Golom, and all the doctors in this hospital, are governed by rules of procedure. Dr. Golom followed those procedures. Mrs. Lefkovitz's death was a result of the injuries she suffered for which she was admitted, not a result of Dr. Golom's actions. He acted ethically and professionally – and he saved the baby."

"There will be hell to pay when we find out who her attackers were," Gershon whispered. "Goddamn it!" he hissed. "I'll kill the sons of bitches, I swear."

"No, you won't, Gershon. I will."

We turned and saw Solomon standing at the entrance to the waiting room. His face was devoid of expression, his eyes lifeless. "I'll be doing the killing," he said calmly. Without waiting for a response, he headed for the stairs.

Gershon raced after him and grabbed him by the arm. "There are police downstairs," he said. "Wait a few minutes until I can talk to them."

"I have a funeral to arrange, Gershon. I don't care about the police."

I approached them. "If you will give me a few minutes, I believe I can get this matter resolved. With Dr. Golom leaving Lodz, I doubt he will want to return for a trial. I'm sure I can persuade him to drop the charges."

Gershon held on to Solomon's arm and nodded to me. I returned to the main floor.

ON THE MORNING of Miriam's funeral the sun shone brightly, but its warmth did little to lessen the chill felt by those assembled. The dirt road that led into the cemetery was lined with wagons, the nearest one black, enclosed and ominous. The bare trees stood silent, their naked branches extending like fingers to the four corners of the horizon, as if inviting the heavens to witness the proceedings. I had come as an observer and stood to one side. I had not been invited, but the tragic events gripped my curiosity and I found myself compelled to attend. Because of my involvement with patients of different religions at the hspital, I knew enough to understand the proceedings. Rabbi Sternberg opened his prayer book and recited from Proverbs:

A woman of valour, who can find?
Far beyond pearls is her value.
Her husband's heart relies on her and he shall lack no fortune.
She repays his good, but never his harm, all the days of her life …

The rabbi's voice trembled with grief as he finished the passage. He had sung the Psalm sweetly and tenderly, bestowing meaning on the reality of what had brought them to this place of final rest. With "Amen" he concluded the prayer and closed his book. Then he addressed the mourners.

"Why, we ask, is a woman in the prime of her life taken from us? Judaism teaches us that every life is precious. We are taught that our Lord God is merciful, compassionate and gracious, slow to anger and abundant in kindness and truth. God in his wisdom and justice chooses to give and He also chooses to take.

"In trying to find a reason for this tragedy, we must not become embittered. We must remember Miriam, not in the darkness of her death but in the light of how she lived and how much she affected those who knew her. Her soul is at rest, but she has left us with more than memories.

"Through her son, Miriam Lefkovitz will always be a part of our lives. For her sake, and the sake of her precious, grieving family, we must focus on life – not death – because only in life can we begin to heal."

Rabbi Sternberg looked at Solomon. Solomon's face registered only anguish as he watched his wife's body being slowly lowered into the cold ground. One by one, the men tossed a few spades of earth into the grave. The rabbi was the last, obscuring the body forever from human sight. When he was finished, he led the mourners away. Solomon and Gershon remained, their eyes fixed on the grave.

Finally, the cemetery workers completed the task started by the mourners and left. Still, Solomon and Gershon remained. I moved to the crown of a nearby hill to see the two men more clearly. The cemetery was now peaceful. The trees rustled gently in the wind, no birds sang, no human voices spoke. Nothing existed but what lay at their feet – a fresh mound of earth, disturbed and raw, a reminder of a life that no longer existed.

I watched Gershon leave Solomon and stop at the gate. He had a faraway look in his eyes. Weeks later when I saw him, he told me what had happened at the site and why he waited at the gate.

They stood looking down at the grave. "It's time to go, Solomon," Gershon said.

Solomon's eyes remained fixed on the grave. "We never think that death is going to happen to us." He spoke softly. "We are born and we die. These things are beyond our control. When other people die, we say 'That's too bad' because it's someone else's tragedy. But when it happens to us, we're never prepared, even though we know that someday it will be our turn. So many things we put off doing until later. So many words we never say, because we assume there will be many years yet to say them."

He fell silent.

"Let's go, Solomon," Gershon repeated and tugged on his arm.

Solomon pushed Gershon's hand away. "Miriam and I met less than two years ago, Gershon. Hardly enough time to understand each other, to say what should be said. Many people have heard me speak. They heard words that made them feel good, even got them excited, but I've never said the words Miriam wanted to hear . . ." His voice trailed off.

Gershon looked worried. "Solomon, we must go." This time he took hold of his arm and led him from the graveside.

Solomon allowed himself to be pulled, but after a few steps, he stopped. His voice was husky and his tears rolled down his face. "She would ask me to say it. I thought it was a game, Gershon, so I teased her and I never said the words. I never told her that I loved her." He began to sob uncontrollably.

Gershon led Solomon back to the grave. Solomon dropped to his knees and placed his hands into the freshly dug earth. "I love you, Miriam," he whispered. "I will always love you." He repeated the words over and over again.

Gershon left and waited for him at the gate. He said he was reconstructing the week's events, putting each piece of the puzzle into its place, knowing when Solomon put aside his grief, the hate would surface and the hunt for the perpetrators would begin.

DR. PODGORSKA FELL silent, his face lost in thought. He raised his head abruptly and looked at his host and smiled, the card still in his hand. He slipped it back into the envelope.

"What! What! That's it? That's not it. That's not the whole story. There must be more."

Dr. Podgorska smiled.

"Let me have that card. I what to see what it said," his host said.

Dr. Podgorska tilted the envelope and the card slipped out. He handed it to his host. It read: *Unforgettable Funeral.*

"You impertinent blighter. You must finish the story! That's part of the bargain."

Dr. Podgorska retrieved his cane from behind his chair and looked down at his host. "Maybe you'll invite me back. Who knows, I might pick a card that says: Hunter's Vengeance." He smiled at the members, then slowly navigated his way through the sea of overstuffed chairs and perplexed expressions.

He stood on the damp London street and laughed. It had been a marvellous evening after all, he thought.

Flight

THE MAN SPED down the narrow stairs and out the front door, slamming it closed behind him. Above, in the now silent, comfortable loft apartment were oil canvasses scattered everywhere. A pallet hung precariously on the edge of a small wooden table and brushes and paint tubes lay strewn on the floor where they had fallen. An unfinished portrait of a beautiful woman leaned on an easel below the large skylight and a single sheet of writing paper lay on the floor amidst the items, half opened at the crease, a delicate script covering less than half its surface.

May 11, 1965

My dearest Matthew:

I wanted to tell you when you were here how I felt, but I couldn't find the right words. I have discharged myself from the hospital. I had to. To be near you is too painful. I sense your guilt, but there should be none. I now understand what it was you asked of me. By the time you read this, I will be far away – too far to return. I beg you not to look for me. We are both blameless. Pity would have destroyed us. Remember me, for I will never forget you. I will always cherish the time we had together.

M.B.

MILES AWAY FROM Toronto, the twilight rays of the sun reflected off the windows of the train as it sped westward through the Rocky Mountains, leaving a ribbon of white smoke behind. Margo Booth stared out her window, watching the sun slowly meet the horizon. She had spent most of the previous day and this day as she was now, with thoughts of regrets, of her bad luck, of decisions she had made that were now beyond change. She was also full of feelings she wanted to cherish. The train entered a long tunnel and the single bulb over her head blinked into momentary darkness. She closed her eyes, sighed and cast her thoughts back, back to the beginning, back before her flight from Matthew – to a life she could no longer have.

THE BALLROOM RESOUNDED with the sounds of music and excited voices. Buyers of fine women's apparel gazed avidly at the runway, praising the garments on the models as they paraded before them. As the last one left the stage, the music beat a familiar rhythm, announcing that Margo Booth, Phillipe deNeuf's top model, was about to appear wearing the designer's most stunning creation of the year.

The curtains parted and Margo, tall, slim, skin the colour of milk, stepped onto the runway wearing a white, strapless, chiffon, cinched-waist evening gown with a full skirt. Her slender fingers moved sensuously, her full lips were parted just enough to show even, white teeth and her eyes sparkled with excitement. She seemed to float to the end of the runway, made a half turn, another half turn and then one more. Her slender hips swayed provocatively as she returned to the curtain, did a pirouette, swirling the hem of her gown above her knees and exposing shapely calves and smooth thighs. Her smile broadened, and then she disappeared through the curtain opening. The audience went wild with appreciation and behind the curtain the makeup staff and dressers added their accolades, knowing the show had been a huge success.

"You were absolutely marvellous!" Philippe said, throwing his arms around Margo. "Marvellous, marvellous, marvellous!"

She smiled. "It's your turn, Philippe," she said, dropping a kiss on his forehead, then pushing him through the curtain. The applause regained its pitch and Margo's smile widened.

"You seem genuinely pleased for him."

Margo faced the speaker, a handsome man, wearing beige trousers, a black turtleneck sweater and an expensive gold chain around his neck.

She knew immediately by his clothes that he wasn't part of the staff. "You're not staff," she said. "How did you get past security?"

He only smiled.

"I'm sorry," she said, "you shouldn't be back here."

"If you're sorry, why must I leave?" His eyes were laughing.

"And who are you?"

"A dedicated admirer of yours."

"Well, dedicated admirer, you'll still have to leave the stage."

"I could get someone to vouch for me, if it will make you feel better."

Margo shook her head slightly, "No, that won't be necessary. I believe you." She glanced at her watch. "If you'll excuse me, I must change into something more casual and mingle with the buyers." She stepped around him and went into her dressing room at the end of the stage. As she closed the door, she glanced back and saw him watching her.

THE TRAIN HURTLED through the night. Margo was barely able to see the trees that hugged the tracks. She changed her position and her reflection appeared on the glass. Not even her cheekbones, she noted, were as they'd been before the accident. Her nose was shorter and had a slight bump in the middle. The scar on her jaw was barely discernable, but she knew it was there. Mentally, she saw herself as she had been, but when she met her reflection again, the face that looked back at her was the one she now owned. She had been a butterfly and was now a moth. A tear trickled down her cheek as her mind worked its way back.

MARGO MOVED FROM buyer to buyer, receiving warm greetings and words of appreciation for her gown and her beauty. Several men made less-than-subtle overtures and Margo grinned as she played the game of cat and mouse. She was the mouse, hinting but not committing, teasing but not accepting, luring each suitor with her eyes. It was a game she had had to become good at if she wanted to control each situation. Her path was blocked by a man.

"How could you ever know if they loved you?"

She recognized him as the one who had spoken to her backstage and smiled. "They're harmless," she said. "Their words are not their real intent."

"What some want is to go to bed with you," he said.

His candor surprised her. "I know," she grinned. "And what is it you want?"

"To be loved for myself."

Margo's smile slipped from her face. "There is love and there is love." Margo gave him a curious look.

A wealthy patron stopped and recognized the stranger.

"Hello, Matthew! When did you get back?"

"Mr. Madison. It's good to see you again. About three months ago."

"Well, I'm glad I bumped into you. I have a project that's perfect for you. Will you call my secretary and make an appointment?"

"Yes, sir. Will tomorrow be all right?"

"Excellent. You're the answer to a prayer. Am I glad you're back."

They shook hands and Mr. Madison continued on his way.

"You apparently know the right people," Margo said. "I'm impressed."

"Would you care to have dinner with me tomorrow night?"

Margo's smile returned. "I'm sorry, not possible. I have other plans. Besides I don't go out with strangers."

"I'm not a stranger. I know you recognized Elliott Madison. You know he's a builder of skyscrapers and multi-million-dollar homes and you saw he knows me."

"Well, then, go out with him."

Matthew laughed.

Margo felt lightheaded, as if she'd had too much wine. Her skin tingled and her face felt warm. She'd never felt like this before. Even her sense of confusion was not unpleasant.

"Why not break your engagement?" Matthew said.

"Why should I?"

"To satisfy your curiosity."

"What makes you think I'm curious?"

He smiled at her.

She chuckled. "You do intrigue me." She paused, unsure who was now the cat and who the mouse. "If I do, will I get to know your last name?"

"No."

Margo studied him for a moment. "I could find out who you are very easily."

"I know, but you won't. You love a mystery."

"I do?"

"I know more about you than you think."

Margo had difficulty keeping a straight face. At last she said, "I've a twilight shoot on Yonge Street tomorrow, outside the Loews Theatre box office. I should be finished by eight. Pick me up there."

"Excellent. I know the ideal place to eat. It's not too far from there."

She smiled. A buyer passed and she took his arm and walked with him to another part of the room, her voice soft and charming, teasing him to make a purchase. When she turned to glance back at the stranger, he was still watching her, a look of satisfaction on his face.

THERE WAS A soft knock on Margo's compartment door. She darkened the room before partly opening the door. A conductor stood at the door with a food tray perched on a small trolley.

"I didn't mean to disturb you, Miss Booth, but I took the liberty of bringing you something to eat."

"Thank you."

"I noticed you haven't left your compartment today and hadn't ordered anything to eat, so I put a tray together."

"You're very considerate."

Margo opened the door and the conductor brought the tray into the compartment.

"How did you know who I was?" she asked.

The conductor seemed embarrassed. "I recognized your name on my list. I've seen your photograph many times in the newspapers."

"I've changed," she said, "since the accident."

"Some." He backed out of the compartment. "You're still very beautiful," he said and hurriedly made his way down the narrow corridor.

Margo closed the door and returned to her chair, ignoring the food. The sun was gone, replaced by the fat face of a full moon. She was surprised to see that the mountain ranges were behind them. She closed her eyes again and as she sorted through her memories, her smile reappeared.

MARGO SAT IN the restaurant booth and stared at him in astonishment, then she grinned and burst out laughing. "You took me to Fran's on a date? I don't believe it."

"The food was the excuse. It's the company I'm feasting on."

She nodded in appreciation. "And I begged off going to a restaurant that would have cost my escort more money than most people make in a week! Who are you, and don't give me that same answer."

"My name is Matthew Cyna."

"The artist? Well, now I'm really flattered. I've admired your paintings for years. In fact, I own one; a small oil."

"It's called, Serenity."

"Uh-oh. You've been checking up on me. Our meeting wasn't an accident."

"No, it wasn't."

"Why?"

"Because I fell in love with you."

"Really. Love as in 'love', or love as in 'sex'?"

He laughed, knowing she was playing with him. "I've met you before, about three months ago."

"We've never met before. Where?"

"The Park Plaza Hotel."

"Yes, I was there. Raising money for one of Philippe's charities. Where were you?"

"Sketching you," he said. "I was staying there until I could find more permanent accommodations. I saw you on stage and returned to my room to get my pad."

"Am I to understand that you fell in love while sketching me?"

"Yes, I guess that's one way of putting it."

She shook her head. "You don't appear dangerous. Are you on leave from a hospital? What you're saying is crazy."

"Anything is possible," he answered. "Do I frighten you with my confession?"

"I'm not sure." She sighed in exasperation. "This is amazing. I'm sitting in a restaurant with a man I've never met who confesses he fell in love with me while sketching my picture. I understand now why you're an artist. You have a vivid imagination."

"It's not my imagination that made me feel this way."

"Well you can't say I encouraged you. I never knew you until this week. Are you not happy doing what you do?"

"Are you happy being a model?"

"Now that's a strange question. Why wouldn't I be happy?"

"Once, perhaps, but not anymore. I watched you on stage. Remember, I'm an artist. Faces are my livelihood. There were moments when I saw the real you and that was not a happy face I looked at." He paused to see the effect of his words. "Modeling has become a game, a dangerous game to you. I see the signs. You're good at make-believe. So was I," he said.

"You think I'm pretending?" she said.

"No, I think you're lying to yourself. Just the way I did."

"I don't know what happened to you, but you must know that a model's life is surreal."

"I disagree. Your world has become a fantasy. You're successful, financially secure and extremely attractive. You have all the ingredients for happiness, but you aren't. So what is it you're missing? Love. Real love. Your life has become a fixture as long as you're beautiful. And when you're no longer as beautiful on the outside, will your lovers see the beauty on the inside? Fantasies always come to an end and when yours does will your life have had any meaning? I think you are at the crossroads and you know it."

"Wow! All this from one sketch."

"No, all this from my own experience. I, too, lived a fantasy. One day, I recognized what I had become. I ran away from that life and went to Tahiti to find myself."

"What brought you back?"

"You can't run away from yourself. Whatever problems we have, they have to be faced."

"And what was it that made you face reality?"

He became solemn before answering. "A bad experience that I thought would affect me for the rest of my life." His smile broadened. "Then I saw you."

"You don't look old enough to have gained the wisdom of the sages."

"I'm eight years older than you are."

"You have been doing your research. Can you be trusted?"

"Would you like to go out with me again?"

Margo stood, a grin on her face. "For cheesecake and coffee? Can you afford it? It has been a long day and I would like to go home. Tomorrow is another heavy schedule. I'll take a cab, big spender." She hesitated. "How do you know I'm not like those other women in your life?"

Matthew smiled. "Your eyes."

Margo headed for the door, then stopped and returned to his table. "I'll be through with my shoot on Thursday at eight. I'll meet you here."

THAT WAS HOW it started. The months flew by quickly as they explored each other's lives. He was wealthy and his artistic talent was in demand, both as an impressionist and a commercial artist. Success had come easily to him and he'd fallen into its trap. Many women had thrown themselves at him. None of his relationships had been permanent though, and there had been many. He drank and took drugs, but instead of becoming euphoric, he became depressed. He would wake the next day and not know where he had been, what he'd done and or even the name of the person lying naked beside him. He spoke haltingly about these interludes, the effects of which were still obvious in his voice. There seemed, however, to be a gap in his story between that old life and his running away, but he never filled it. Whatever it was that caused him to reclaim his life, he kept it a secret. But it had changed his life.

She knew that sex, in time, would enter into their relationship, but he never pursued it. She found that curious. Margo wanted him. She waited for him to begin the process, eager to be in his arms, to feel his body on her, his hands caressing her skin. She waited until she could wait no longer. One night, after he brought her home, she took the initiative and kissed him.

They touched.

They undressed.

When they lay beside each other on the bed, she knew what had been missing from his story. "What's wrong?" Margo said as she covered her nakedness with the sheet, confusion and disappointment on her face. She watched him leave the bed. "When you said love, you didn't mean physical love, did you?" she said.

"No."

"What did you expect from me?"

He stood beside the bed. "Understanding," he answered.

"What caused this to happen?"

"The drugs I used to take. It might come back. I've been told that there is nothing the matter with me. It's psychological."

"I don't understand."

"Can love not survive without sex? I had hoped you would accept me for myself. I knew this moment would come and I hoped that I could give you what love I could, in the only way I could."

"I'm confused. I have to think about it. But I do love you, Matthew Cyna," Margo whispered.

"I know. But enough?"

SHE THOUGHT SHE could forget him if she didn't see him, but that was not to be. She was tempted many times over the next few months to go to his loft apartment, but didn't have the courage. Love and sex were intertwined in her mind. She had difficulty separating one from the other. She was thirty-two, at the height of her career, and her ideas of love and desire confused her. Each passing week, the battle to give in to her feelings gained momentum. One rainy evening, as she was about to enter a cab outside her apartment, she saw him standing across the street, tucked into an alcove, watching her. She stared at him, her hand on the door of the cab, unable to make herself enter. Then, without further thought, she raced across the busy intersection. All her confusion had disappeared. She knew what she wanted. She saw the oncoming car, but it was too late. She heard herself scream his name just before the impact. There was a moment of pain when she was struck; her body was slammed into the pavement; her face and nose smashed against the curb. She felt his hands and heard her name, then nothing.

The weeks in the hospital were slow in passing. Reconstructive surgery resulted in a smile that was crooked and a nose that was plain. Many more weeks passed, long, difficult weeks as her broken arm and leg healed. She knew her career was over. She no longer cared. Crossing the street had been her awakening. She no longer wanted the artificial life she'd lived, but a life of being loved by Matthew. Phillippe wanted her to come back, not as a model, but to work with him. She had said no.

When she looked in the mirror, she didn't recognize the image. At first it made her cry, but in time she came to accept her new face. Did Matthew? After the accident, he was there day and night. With her face bandaged, she felt his touch, heard his words of love, felt his presence give her the strength to overcome the pain and depression. When the bandages came off, she sensed something was not right. He would smile when he entered her room, kiss her, but there was no life in his lips. They were soft, tasteful, polite. And then came the time when the words he didn't say hurt more than what he did say.

"Hi," she said when he came into her room about two months after the accident.

"How are you?" he asked, his voice almost a monotone.

"Getting better. And you?"

"Oh, busy. A lot on my mind."

"Wouldn't like to change places, would you?" she asked jokingly. He never answered the question but went to the window and peered out.

"The marks on your face are going away," he said, turning to look at her.

"Most of them. Some are permanent. I try not to think about them."

His eyes seemed to look through her, not at her. "I see in the newspaper you're doing a portrait for Julie Cabot," she said.

He nodded. "She's very demanding."

"She's rich and beautiful."

"Yes, she is."

"She's a trophy hunter. She likes men."

Matthew turned his back to her and stared out the window. The silence between them was heavy. "I don't think I'm the kind of trophy she's looking for," he said, almost in a whisper.

He stayed for only an hour. The next day and the next were no different. He seemed too anxious to leave. Now she was filled with painful questions and afraid of the unspoken answers. Days would pass when he wouldn't appear. He claimed it was his work and he would make up for it when his contract with Julie Cabot ended. Was this an excuse? Was it love he still felt or guilt, and if it was guilt, would resentment follow? She sensed their love was over. She decided to leave Toronto and him, so the memories she had would not be tarnished by arguments and bitter words.

MARGO OPENED HER eyes. It took a few minutes for her to realize she must have fallen asleep. She felt the train slowing down and looked out the window. They had reached Vancouver. When the train eased into the station, she watched the people on the platform and felt a sense of envy at their ease. She placed her clothes into her suitcase and waited. There was a knock at her door. She looked to see if she had everything and then opened it to the conductor.

"Good morning," he said, smiling. "I thought you might need help with your bags."

"Yes, I do. And could you arrange for a cab to take me to Pier 17?"

"Going on a cruise, ma'am?"

"No, on a journey. A slow journey to a place where someone I know found himself."

"Yes, ma'am." He brought her luggage out into the narrow corridor and took it off the train. Margo followed.

MATTHEW LOOKED OUT the airplane window at the clouds below, occasionally glimpsing the peaks of the Rocky Mountains. He prayed he was not too late. He glanced at his watch. It had taken him two days to find out where Margo had gone. Her landlord had finally told him. Margo had been right about Julie Cabot. She was more interested in trying to seduce him than cooperating. That was why he went to his doctor. He actually felt his body react and it frightened him. He couldn't tell Margo. What if it meant nothing? The doctor was confident his body was healing itself. He was overjoyed. When he decided to tell her, she seemed preoccupied with what had happened to her. Did she blame him for her injuries? Had the accident taken away the love she felt? Why had his body returned only to be confronted with the loss of the one he loved? Those were the questions that had plagued him, questions that had no answers until he got the letter.

He was not going to lose her.

Under Suspicion

TWO BARTENDERS POURED drinks as fast as the servers placed their orders, their stern faces concentrating on what they were doing and at those sitting at the long bar. The noisy tavern, the smoke-filled, crowded room, the loud music, muted television – the scene appeared normal, except to Patrick O'Hare, the older of the bartenders. He'd been watching a man in a business suit, in his late fifties, sitting alone at the far end of the bar, a full glass of beer clutched in one hand, a solemn look on his tired face. His gaze forever wandered around the room, either searching or watching. Patrick wasn't sure which, but he was certain that this man had a mission and what it might be worried him. He'd seen that look before in Ireland and it was generally followed by something bad.

Boisterous laughter rang throughout the narrow, smoke-filled room, drowning out the tunes that blared from a modern jukebox in the corner. Noisy patrons drifted between the crowded tables, passing remarks to friends and acquaintances, shouting to be heard. Television sets suspended from the ceiling at the four corners of the room showed muted images of baseball players' anxious faces as they strove to prove themselves to yet another noisy crowd of fans. The man appeared oblivious to the noise, the jostling and the merrymaking, his gaze constantly shifting to his wristwatch, the front door and the crowd. He loosened his tie and undid the top button on his shirt, then pulled the beer towards him, then pushed it back to where it had been. The longer Patrick watched him, the more he became convinced his thoughts were accurate. Something wasn't right. The man had been sitting for more than half an hour and had yet to even take a sip of his beer. Patrick had too many years watching patrons under his belt not to sense trouble. The man leaned over and stared at the floor as if looking for something, then he straightened himself and continued to look about.

"What're you lookin' at?" Molly, the barmaid asked him. Her Irish accent made her words sound musical. She placed her tray on the bar and flexed her fingers. Her brow was moist with perspiration and her skin shone with the sheen of polished wood. "Somethin' interesting?"

Patrick nodded his head toward the man. "Don't like what I see," he said.

Molly turned her gaze to the end of the bar. "I don't see anything wrong. What should I be lookin' for?" she said.

"That man's not drinking and he's got something on his mind that's causing him to be nervous. He's jumpy. I got this feeling somethin's going down. Something bad."

"Like what?"

"That full glass of beer has been in his hand for more'n thirty minutes. Why's he here if he ain't drinking?"

Molly looked again at the man and shook her head. "Looks harmless."

"So does a bomb until it goes off."

Molly's expression of curiousity turned to skepticism. "If he's a bomb, at his age it must be tickin' awfully slow. Three pints of Guinness, my suspicious bucko, and easy on the foam. The patrons are complaining." She smiled teasingly.

"Very funny. I'm no rookie, cookie."

"You ain't no poet either." Molly glanced at the man again before hurrying off with her order. Patrick continued to stare at him. "You're trouble waitin' to happen," he muttered to himself under his breath. "I can smell it."

Molly returned. "Still watching him, are you?"

"He keeps glancing at his watch. He's either waiting for someone – or waiting to leave at a certain time. Did you notice if there was a bag or a box by his feet?"

"And pray tell, why would there be something like that at his feet?"

The bartender leaned over and whispered, "Are you daft? A bomb, Molly, a bomb."

Molly glared at Patrick in annoyance. "You're the one that's daft. This is Canada, not Ireland. You've brought the disease here with you, I can see."

"What disease might that be?"

"Hate and suspicion. I think you're making something out of nothing. Now, before you expound on your runaway thoughts, why don't you just go over to him and ask if it's a sympathetic ear he wants? That's part of your job, is it not? He does look troubled."

"Why don't you, Molly, girl? It's you that thinks he might be in need of coddling. And for your information, my nose has sniffed out many a suspicious character in the homeland."

Molly laughed. "More than likely it was dirty underwear and a filthy mind you smelled. And chances were, they were your own."

"Is that a nice thing to say, Molly? You know my heart beats for you."

"Really. And here it was something else I thought was throbbing." Molly started to walk toward the end of the bar.

"Molly, where you goin'?"

"To test your nose," she said.

MOLLY STOPPED BESIDE the man. He looked up and smiled. Molly smiled back. "Is there something the matter with the beer, Mister?" she asked.

The man's expression showed his surprise. He looked down at the glass in front of him. "Should there be?"

"I would hope to hell not. That's as good a Guinness as you'll get anywhere this side of the Atlantic." Molly gave him a closer look. "You're not Irish, are you?"

"No, I'm sorry, I'm not."

"Well, don't take it to heart. Not all of us can be so lucky." She laughed, a sound of pure delight.

The man first smiled, then laughed with her. His smile returned as he looked into Molly's emerald eyes. "I can tell by your eyes that you're here for a reason, young lady. Am I sitting too long at the bar?"

"You can sit here all night for all I care. It's the glass of beer you're not drinking that brought me."

"I'm not much on drinking beer."

"Then pray tell, why are you here, if you don't mind me askin'?"

He gave her a curious look. "I have my reasons," he said. "Why are you asking?"

Molly leaned closer to him so no one would overhear. "My friend the bartender thinks you got a bomb at your feet." She pointed to the black attaché case beside his stool. "He's worried because you keep looking at your watch and aren't drinking."

The man's eyes opened wide. "No, not really! You don't believe that, do you?" he said, a worried look on his face.

"No, but you make me curious. If you ain't drinkin' why you here?"

The man smiled slowly. "To celebrate an anniversary of a kind."

"Not a happy one, I would think from the look on your face."

"Yes and no. It's a long story that ended at precisely 8:32 in the evening on this date many years ago," he said. He appeared a bit uncomfortable with the admission.

Molly smiled and her eyes seemed to twinkle. "Is it a story you can tell to me?"

He swung his gaze to the door before answering. "It's kind of personal," he said.

"Are you waiting for someone?"

"Yes. By this time, I'm usually in a restaurant with a glass of beer ready to make a toast. It's the only time I drink beer."

"Then tell me, why aren't you in one now?"

"A late meeting." He indicated with his head toward the black case. "Couldn't get up north in time."

"Instead of a restaurant, you've come to Casey's Bar, have you?" Molly laughed loudly and glanced at Patrick watching with eyes that she was sure he hoped were ears. She edged closer to the man. "I'm a good judge of people. Been serving beer since I left school. I can tell you've a story in you. Care to share it with me. I love a good story."

"There's no bomb in my story, but, yes, there's a story," he said, smiling. "Do you do this often?"

"Ah! I hear stories every night until my poor ears go deaf, but me thinks yours is one I would like to hear. So loosen up and talk to me."

The smile broadened. The man glanced at the bartender and then at Molly. "It's not what you think," he said.

The stool next to him was empty and Molly plopped herself down on it. "It never is. Go on, you're wasting time." She looked at his watch. "You have less than twenty minutes to share your story. I think if it were any longer, my friend Patrick would be rushing over here with a bucket of water. I can see in the mirror he hasn't taken his eyes off us. Let's make him hang a little bit longer. How about it – are you going to share your story?" Molly's smile was so broad, if it had been any wider, it would have escaped off her face. "Time is wasting. I think Patrick is squinting."

The man laughed. "All right," he said.

"HAVE YOU EVER stood in front of a mirror and realized the image looking back at you was not you any more. That happened to me. When I was young, I worked long hours building a business and my wife worked alongside me. It was an adventure we both shared. After awhile, though, the business no longer needed my wife's involvement. My wife and I became strangers. I always worked. She joined a women's community volunteer group."

The man glanced at his watch and a worried look appeared on his face. He returned his gaze to Molly and smiled. "I warned you, it wasn't what you thought," he said.

"I've heard a lot of stories. Sad ones most times. Yours is starting out that way. I had hoped it would be a happy one."

He didn't answer. His hand reached out to the glass of beer and drew it closer to him, his gaze on the black liquid inside. He gave a huge sigh. "Do you know how two people fall out of love?" He looked up at Molly, but continued without waiting for her answer. "At least one lives a lie. In this case, it was me." He seemed to expect Molly to interrupt, but Molly remained silent. He continued. "At the beginning, I wasn't aware that I had changed. When I was home, I would be in my study long after my wife went to bed, working on some papers that didn't get done at the office and often when we were supposed to attend one of her service functions, I would beg off at the last moment claiming an overload of work. I pretended that what I was doing was for the two of us – but that wasn't true. I wanted success and money meant success and to get money I felt I had to immerse myself in my business. Everything else became expendable. My wife and I had become two separate people sharing a house and, unfortunately, we had no children to share our lives.

"When I reached that level of success I had been striving for, I discovered to my surprise that accolades and money did not mean happiness. There were times I would stand before the bathroom mirror in the morning and stare at myself, questioning the road I had taken. What had happened to the dreams and to the family I wanted, I asked myself? How had I gotten side-tracked?" He paused as if he had asked himself this question many times before and was still searching for the words to answer.

"Well, you know, Mister, yours is an old story," Molly said. "I could point out several in this room who are living it now."

The man nodded.

"And then everything changed because of a telephone call. It was early in the morning and I hadn't left for the office yet." He paused, his eyes clouded, as he seemed stuck in his words. "Karen answered it." There was a long pause before he continued. "After a few minutes of listening, her face paled and her voice broke as she spoke to the person on the other end. I could tell it was bad news. After she replaced the telephone, she began to cry softly. 'What is it?' I asked."

"A close friend of mine has discovered a lump under her arm," she said.

Patrick approached, his eyes roaming about where the man sat. "Molly," he said. "Your customers are askin' for you."

Molly swung around to look at her work area and saw some of the patrons waving their glasses. She stepped off the stool. "I'll be right back," she said. "Don't you go anywhere."

The man smiled.

Patrick watched Molly leave and was about to return to where he always stood, but instead asked. "Are you staying much longer?"

The smile on the man's face broadened and he leaned closer to Patrick. "I'm waiting for a bag to be delivered to me," he said.

Patrick gave him his fishy look, pursed his lips and frowned. "Are you now?"

The man nodded. Patrick withdrew to his section and continued to watch him and the door. The man smiled at him, then gazed toward the door, too, then back to his watch.

Molly placed her empty tray on the bar and hurried to the man, who had a cell phone against his ear. She plopped down on her stool. "Are you being stood up?" she asked.

He put the cell back in his pocket. "I doubt that. Just worried the time is getting close."

"If the time was so important, why'd you change your business meeting?"

His eyes twinkled. "It's a surprise."

"It certainly would be if whoever you're waiting for doesn't show.

All right, you were saying your wife's friend found a lump. What happened next?"

"Well, I tried reassuring her that everything would be fine, but she offered me a weak smile and went into our bedroom to be alone. Joan Dixon was her best friend. They were as opposite as the proverbial two peas in a pod. Karen always took everything so seriously and was reluctant to draw attention to herself while her friend, on the other hand, radiated natural charm and sparkled with life. She was effervescent, bubbly. Energy in motion.

"They had met at a community program. Karen was at her seat when Joan entered and sat beside her. Joan introduced herself." He stopped, glanced at his watch again and then at the front door. "I'm sorry. I hope nothing happened."

"C'mon man," Molly said. "You can't leave me hanging like this."

He grinned. "I don't even know your name."

"It's my name you would be wantin'? It's Molly. Molly Donahue, originally from Kildaree County. And now that you know me name, are you going to finish your story?"

"You have a way with you, Molly Donahue. I have never told anyone what I'm telling you and you're right, it feels good."

"There you are. I've done me a good deed. No more interruptions if you don't mind. Finish your story."

The man took a deep breath and continued. "They became friends, and over the years Joan encouraged Karen to extend herself beyond the boundaries she was comfortable with, ultimately rising through the organization's executive to become its president. It was a gradual and satisfying evolution, all because of Joan Dixon. I played no role in her development.

"And now, it was Joan who needed encouragement.

"Joan underwent tests and they were together often while waiting for the results. They reminisced, laughed and cried. Karen offered reassurances that the lump would prove benign, even though she feared the worst. The tests results were not good and surgery was scheduled immediately. Over the next few months, Joan's life changed dramatically from that of an independent businesswoman, wife and mother, to someone whose life depended on others. Week after week, Karen visited her friend, and each visit took its toll on Karen. Joan was a fighter. She slowly regained her health; the chemotherapy had put the cancer into remission."

The man pulled his glass to him and lifted it, seeing his reflection in the liquid inside. "That's when the face in the mirror looked back at me and I wondered who he was? I quietly changed my life. I came home more often. Karen and I talked about the way it used to be. It was at this time that a mammogram indicated one of Karen's breasts had a suspicious shadow and needed further investigation.

"I accompanied Karen to the doctor's office and her worst suspicions were confirmed. Despite our efforts to prepare ourselves for bad news, fear took possession of Karen – fear of the unknown, fear of death. And shame. Would she be mutilated? She had seen all this while Joan had undergone her treatments. Uncertainty ate at her as the cancer chewed from within. Could she go through what her friend had? Questions she had no answers for nibbled at her strength even before she began her treatments.

"And I floundered, not knowing how to respond." He paused, his gaze on the glass of beer in his hand, his eyes moist, as he seemed to fight back the feelings in him.

Molly quietly waited.

He took a deep breath before continuing. "Joan, however, did. She refused to let Karen wallow in her fear, reminding her that each day was too precious to waste. I found myself a witness to a drama in which my role was as supporting actor while the main characters played out a scene of life and death. Joan willed Karen to get better – and in time, fortunately, she did. But not long after, Joan's cancer returned and a few short months later she died . . . and that's my story."

"What is it that happened at 8:32?" Molly asked.

The man met Molly's gaze directly. "It's when she died. On this day, twenty-three years ago."

"Is it your wife you're waitin' for?"

"Yes," he answered. "As a rule we go out together, but I had this meeting downtown and she selected this place. She doesn't know it, but I sold my company tonight. I wanted it to be today."

"Did you now."

"We've had many good years." He looked at his watch. "It's almost 8:32."

A woman in her fifties hurriedly approached them. "I'm not late, am I?" she asked.

"Just in time," he said.

Molly slipped off the stool and returned to the bartender.

"Are those tears in your eyes, Molly?" he asked.

"No. It's this awful smoke," she said.

"He's talking to a woman," the bartender said. "I think he's making a toast."

Molly didn't turn to look.

"He's drinking the beer now," the bartender said. "And so is she."

"And why shouldn't they? It's good beer."

"What are they drinking to, Molly?"

Molly dabbed at her eyes. "To a memory."

"They're holding hands. At their age, I woulda thought that was past tense."

"I'd be thinking your nose needs cleaning and your heart could do with a scrubbing as well."

"Really. Well, lass, I've told you before, if you listened to my heart, I think you'd find it's beating your name."

Molly gave the bartender a suspicious look. "If that's not blarney, I don't know what is. Take another look at those two and tell me what you see."

The bartender gazed again at the couple. "I see two old people acting peculiar."

"No, you big clod! What you see is two young people who have grown old together. You can't see love?"

The bartender looked again. "The woman just kissed the man and is hugging him."

"I'm so glad you've got your eyesight. My advice to you is to tell your heart to pump another tune. It's not my beat." Molly picked up her empty tray and disappeared into the crowd.

The bartender stared down the bar at the man again. "I knew you were going to be trouble," he said, "and I was right."

A Dog-Gone Crime

The Harvey Shulman Case
A Gabe Garshowitz Mystery

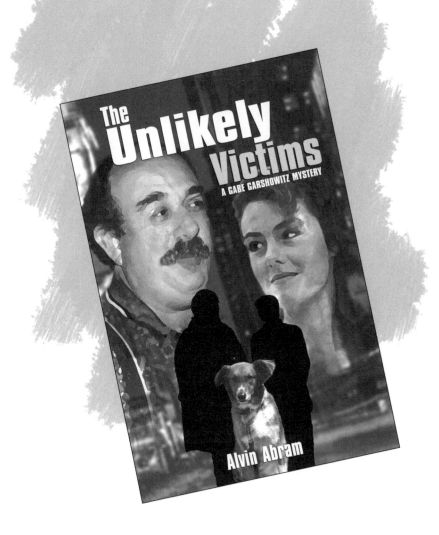

THE FULL MOON cast an almost eerie glow on the parkland. The air was crisp and penetrating. Heavily weighted with age, bare trees rustled ever so slightly. Crusted in their thick coats of bark, they looked like sentinels over the surrounding emptiness. The silence was suddenly broken by an object striking the hardened earth, followed by a human grunt. Over and over it occurred, more insistently now. A flashlight shone for a brief moment, then an axe was picked up and the earth struck repeatedly. Each successive blow widened and deepened the elongated hole. The pick was replaced with a shovel and the hole grew as the softer earth was freed from its place.

The digger stopped when he heard the sounds of an oncoming vehicle. He lay down in the hole, concealing himself, and waited. He saw a thin beam of light shine from the window of the car. Police. It was the police scanning the grounds for intruders. The vehicle inched nearer, the beam swinging in several directions, then the vehicle passed the cluster of trees and disappeared around the bend in the park road. A few minutes later it returned, moving faster, and continued back to the entrance.

The first sprinkling of snow began to fall as the digger pulled himself out of the hole and dragged forward a large tube-like shape. With much effort, he finally laid it alongside the hole. Pausing only a moment to catch his laboured breath, he rolled the tube into the hole, then replaced the disturbed earth until the ground appeared smooth. He stomped on the earth and then shovelled more into place and stomped it flat. Whatever soil was left, he spread over a wider area. The snow was falling faster and soon would cover the churned earth. With luck, time would remove all traces of what he had buried.

With axe and shovel in hand, he left the park and headed to his car in the parking lot of the large grocery store across the street. The balaclava insulated his head and his heavy work clothes kept out the cold, but still, when he reached the car, he was shivering. He unlocked the trunk and threw the tools inside. Snow had already covered the surface of the road and, according to the weather forecast, by daylight would be centimetres deep. He started the car and drove away.

MY NAME IS Detective Gabe Garshowitz. I'm sixty years old and a thirty-year veteran of the Toronto police force, twenty of them in homicide. My partner is Iris Forester; five-eight, attractive – too attractive for a cop, short hair, brunette, with bright eyes and an engaging smile. She has a black belt in martial art and gets pissed when I call her "sweetie." In fact, she gets pissed when anyone calls her "sweetie." She's also the niece of Superintendent Greg Holloway, my boss and previous partner. Earlier in the year, the position opened with the leave of the previous superintendent due to ill health and I was asked if I wanted to take the exam. I said no, so they asked Greg. Lost him, gained his niece.

Iris and I entered the precinct room after spending the morning in court waiting to be called in as witnesses in a murder case. It was a wasted time. The accused changed his plea from not guilty to guilty. His lawyer had worked out a plea bargain. By saving the city money, the prosecutor agreed to a lesser charge. It wasn't the first time and I guess it won't be the last. Our courts were so bogged down that economics played a big role in determining punishment, and yet the stats still said there was less crime. I didn't believe it.

I was tired. Not the usual tiredness from long hours and short sleep, but the weariness that comes from living with constant pain. The initial diagnosis was I had a Baker's Cyst under my left knee. What's a Baker's cyst I asked? An inflammation between the joints that contracts and expands as I use my leg, brought on by normal wear and tear, overweight and a sudden move from a sitting or kneeling position. The doctor was telling me I was old, fat and sedentary. I've discovered that doctors are beginning to talk like lawyers. No amount of aspirin was any help. I was onto Tyenol 3 now and that only brought temporary relief. I was asked to see a therapist and do exercise to see if the cyst would break off and dissolve on its own. I love the way specialists tell people what to do but never how. Did he think I had a desk job? Whatever the problem, it wasn't going away. I threw myself into my chair and suppressed a groan. Or thought I had.

"Have you seen a doctor, Gabe?"

I gave Iris my blank look that said what are you talking about? "For what?"

"Your knees."

I looked at my knees and tried to say something funny. "I'm quite attached to them."

"You got something wrong, Gabe. You're in pain. I watched you in court. You were always rubbing your knees and you walk like a lumbering truck. Why aren't you seeing a doctor?"

"There's nothing wrong. I twisted my knee somehow. It'll go away."

"I told Howard about you."

"Howard? Howard Claremont? You seeing the patrol cop?"

"Yeah, I'm seeing him. I described the way you walk and he thinks you got arthritis. That can cripple you if not treated."

"Shit! Did you tell your uncle, too?"

"No, Gabe. Go see a doctor."

Superintendent Holloway entered the room and headed our way. I looked at Iris and she gave me a look of defiance.

"And lose some weight," she whispered as Holloway stopped at our desk.

"Good idea, Gabe. You're putting on the pounds. At your age, it's harder to lose. If you're not careful, you could end up with arthritis. And that hurts."

"You're not giving us another case, are you?" I asked.

"Yep. Just came in and so did the two of you. A patrol answered a call from a woman who was complaining about a barking dog. Apparently the woman had gone to the house next door to ask the owner to make his dog stop barking when she noticed what looked like blood between the front door and the screen door. She knocked and rang the bell, but there was no answer, only the dog still barking. The patrol went over to see what's what. They rang the bell, but no answer. They called it in just in case. Here's the address. Have fun."

"C'mon, Greg," I pleaded, "Send Munz. Iris and I got enough going on and now you want us to waste time on one that might be a snoop and scoop for a dog that's been left inside too long. This is ideal for Munz. He's a real shithead."

Greg laughed. "Gabe, you should have been a stand-up comedian. Stop complaining. You're getting to sound like an old man."

"Sixty is not old," I said. I gave him my best dirty look, while Iris grinned. I turned to her. "What's so funny? Your uncle made a bad joke and you think it's funny? Well, sweetie, maybe you want to go by yourself – Uncle Holloway won't mind – and let me know what happens. I'll work on finishing these files alone."

Her face lost its grin quickly. "Don't call me sweetie." She stood and peered down at me. "Maybe you should go with Munz. The way you two bark at each other, this sounds like the ideal case for the two of you."

"You've no sense of humour."

"Let's go. You could use the exercise."

I got to my feet slowly. "I exercise every day."

"Yes, I know, when you push yourself away from the food."

I ignored this and headed for the door.

Toronto is not like New York, Chicago or Los Angeles; the city only gets about fifty homicides a year, with the murderers most often identified and arrested. In any event, getting another case while we were already working on one was one more case than I wanted, and my damn knees were killing me.

Outside, I waited by the car for Iris. "You drive." We got in the car and pulled away.

"You've been to a doctor, haven't you?" she said.

"You're pushing."

"Are you taking stupid pills?"

I ignored the question.

"What did he say?"

"I maybe got a cyst. Watch where you're driving. That white stuff on the road isn't dandruff, it's snow. Lots of it." It was still snowing. Had been off and on since last night. "Do you know where you're going?" I had the slip of paper.

"Yes. Do you know what you're doing?"

For the rest of the trip there was silence.

THE GAWKERS WERE already out in droves. The house was a two-storey with a bedroom over the garage. A couple of patrol cars were waiting for us. One of the cops took us to the door and showed us the rust-coloured stains between the door and the screen. I was pretty sure it was blood. I rang the bell a few times. The dog answered. I told the cop to radio for a search warrant and to call Forensics.

I turned to Iris. "Walk around the property and see if everything's kosher."

"You coming?" I could see she was still pissed off.

"Uh, I'll wait in the car for the search warrant."

She cast a look around and must have seen what I saw. Her face smoothed out and she smiled. "Good idea. I'll meet you there." I watched her trudge into the drifts that were piled next to the house, taking huge exaggerated steps as she made her way around the back.

I went to the car and waited. The search warrant and Iris showed up at the same time. "Anything?" she asked.

"Yes. Suspicious tracks. Two sets. I figured they were squirrels."

The dog continued to make a racket. He had better tonsils than a baritone – I assumed it was a he. The woman who had made the call had come to the car while I waited. She was concerned. She told me the dog was a collie named Mystic. Well, she said, most of him was collie. I broke the panel of glass in the door, reached in and unlocked it, letting it swing all the way open. There was no dog in sight and no smell. Which, at least, meant that no body was decomposing. The owner of the house was about sixty, his neighbour had said. A widower, no kids, lived alone. Alone, unless you counted the dog. The neighbour said they were devoted to each other.

The barking was coming from the second floor.

"I think that's the master bedroom," Iris said. "It's over the garage."

I told one of the cops to stay by the door. Iris went ahead of me, her hand on her holster, the revolver still inside. I don't know what she was expecting. Never heard of a dog packing a gun. We stood outside the bedroom door: Iris, me, and behind us, three patrol cops. Iris quickly opened the door and jumped in. The dog bounded out and raced down the stairs.

"Close the front door!" I yelled.

I heard the door shut. The dog skidded to a stop, turned and raced down the hall. Two of the cops chased after him while Iris and I entered the bedroom. The other cop stayed by the door. It was a two room bedroom. There was no one in the room with the bed, but it was a mess. While the furniture seemed intact, small items were scattered about the floor; fragile decorations lay in disarray, some broken, others cracked. The bed was messed up. The second room was a sitting room;

roll-top desk, swivel chair, long L-shaped couch and a low glass table in front of the television. A closer inspection of the table showed blood on the edge; some had run onto the floor. I went back to the stairs and shouted, "Did someone catch the dog?"

"Yes," came the answer.

"Put a leash on him and take him out to the backyard. He needs to poop. Don't let go of the leash," I shouted. I turned to the cop at the bedroom door. "Nobody in until Forensics gets here."

He nodded.

"You know something about dogs," Iris said. "I'm impressed. I thought you were only an expert on food."

I smiled. "Being a woman, you wouldn't understand. As a man, it's a dog's life we sometimes have to lead."

"Shit!"

"Exactly what he's doing."

"God help me," Iris lamented.

"He did. He brought me into your life."

Iris shook her head. "Yeah, I'm really blessed."

FORENSICS CAME AND Iris and I let them do their thing while we questioned the neighbours to get an idea who the owner was and what might have happened. The owner's name was Harvey Shulman. His wife died eight years earlier of cancer and he had no kids. An electrician by trade, he had his own company until he became sick with a heart ailment about five years ago and sold it about a year afterwards. Retired. Good neighbour. Puttered in his garden in the summer, took long walks with his dog. Bought the dog about a year after his wife died.

"The perfect way to pass the years," Iris said.

"That's what I would do if I had to retire: get a dog and make a lasting friend. Dogs are the ideal companions, loyal, devoted, sincere and sympathetic. They can sense their master's pain and somehow are able to share it. Having a pet has been known to lower the owner's blood pressure and combat depression."

"Well, this is a side of you I've never seen," Iris said. "There's actually more to the man than I suspected."

I grimaced. "Let's see what Forensics has found out. We still don't know if there's been a murder. An absent owner is not a crime."

"How about the blood?"

"Could have had an accident, maybe drove himself to the hospital."

"No tire tracks leading into or away from the garage, unless he went before the snowfall last night. He obviously did not leave since."

"I figured that out already. I just wanted to see if you picked it up," I said.

Iris grinned at me. "You'll never change. You know, it's a big house for only one person."

I nodded. "Could have stayed to be with the memories. If he did, he must have had a happy marriage."

Stella Morgan was handling the Forensics team. We went up to her as she was writing something on her clipboard.

"Hi, guys," Stella said. "This won't take that long. I'll have the whole report for you later tonight."

"Whaddaya got?"

"Someone must have spilled a lot of blood."

"A lot? Where?" I asked.

"On the carpet," Stella answered with a grin.

"What carpet?" I asked.

"The one that's gone. Those three white circles on the floor near the table edge are spots of blood. There's a large gap and the blood appears again ten feet away."

"How d'you know there was a carpet?" Iris asked.

Stella pointed to the floor. "Hardwood floor usually means a scatter rug or centre carpet. The floor, according to my measurements, is unscarred for an area that measures five feet by five feet. This is a big bedroom. There's lots of dead space. No pun intended."

I looked at the floor that had been marked off and saw the unmarred surface as compared to the area near the table and television. "You figure a body was rolled in the carpet and taken out."

"That's my guess."

"What about the mess in here?" Iris asked.

"The dog," Stella answered. "Must have been locked in after the fact and went into a frenzy trying to get out. Ran all over the room.

Some of the furniture was moved, but I don't believe because of a fight. My guess is, it was deliberately moved. Both rooms are a mess. It's unlikely a fight would cover that wide an area, especially when one of the opponents is a guy sixty years old with a bad heart."

"How bad?" Iris asked.

"Medicine cabinet in the bathroom indicates bad enough. Nitro patches, blood pressure pills, water pills, cholesterol pills. I'd say he had a congestive heart condition."

"Anything else?" I asked.

"I'll get you his blood type later, otherwise you got the best of it."

"Thanks," I said. I turned to Iris. "Let's go back to headquarters and see if there's any next of kin." We went downstairs. The dog was facing the front door and pulling on his leash; the cop was obviously having a hard time restraining him. "This dog wants out," he said.

"Did he do his business?" I asked.

"Yeah, but he still wants out."

"Did you wipe off his paws when he came back in?"

"You're kidding me, right?"

I bent down and held one of his paws in my hand. They were wet. "Should wipe his paws dry," I said. I left them and went into the kitchen, picked up a dish towel lying beside the sink and returned with it to wipe his paws. The dog looked at me, but still pulled on his leash.

"What we going to do with him?" Iris asked.

"Dog pound, I guess," I answered.

"Can we keep him?"

"Where?"

"Headquarters. Until we find a next of kin."

"You going to take care of him?" I asked.

"Who me? Nope. You!"

"Got no time."

"Bull! I saw the way you looked at him. Couldn't you take him home until we can give him to a member of Shulman's family?"

"Maybe they won't want him."

"Stop with the excuses. You gonna have him put in a cage until someone claims him? Haven't you got a heart?"

"I ain't got time," I replied. "You take him."

"I know nothing about dogs. You do."

With that she strode out of the house, leaving me with the officer – and the dog. I looked at the animal and he gazed up at me dolefully. I ground my teeth and grabbed the leash.

HARVEY SHULMAN HAD one living relative – a younger brother. Further checking showed they'd been partners until their electrical company was dissolved. They contracted their services to developers to wire commercial and residential buildings under construction. According to the records, Melville was three years Harvey's junior. Iris called him and told him that his brother, Harvey, was missing.

She hung up the telephone and gave me a look that said something was fishy.

"They don't talk to each other, right?" I said.

"How'd you know?"

"Don't have any brothers or sisters, do you?"

"No. What's that got to do with it?"

"There's hardly a family that doesn't have someone not talking to someone. The reason brothers and sisters fight is simple – it's too easy to get mad. Often it's petty jealousy that magnifies into justification by one and resentment by the other. I've seen my share. If it wasn't for the business, the two more than likely would be at each other's throats. They saw each other almost every day for most of their lives and built a relationship between them around their business. When the business was dissolved, there was nothing to tie them together. The question is, which one was the bad guy? My guess it's Melville. Good guys like dogs. Mind you, Adolf Hitler liked dogs."

"Did you just make this up?"

"I have a brother who lives in the States. I see him two, three times a year. I'm a cop, he's a salesman; no common ground and no friction. He's happily married, two kids, a nice house, large mortgage, works long hours and has a boring life that pleases him. I'd die before I'd imitate him. When I visit, my nephews call me Uncle Gabe. To them I'm just the screwball Canadian uncle who lives with Eskimos in a cold country, and to me they're nice kids as long as I only see them a couple times a year. Thank God for differences. All right, sweetie, what did Melville Shulman say?"

Iris picked up the telephone and feigned throwing it at me. She scowled fiercely.

"Put it down – it's attached to the floor. Okay, okay, I forgot. I won't call you sweetie anymore . . . today." I grinned.

Iris rolled her eyes.

"It's only a word."

"It's demeaning and patronizing."

"*Oy!* What did Melville say?" I repeated.

She put the telephone down and pecked on her computer, ignoring me.

"Are you giving me the silent treatment? I don't believe it. See how easy it is to get mad?"

Iris gave in. "He said, 'I hope he's not dead. He owes me money. After he pays me, he can drop dead.'"

"Affectionate."

"Mean-spirited."

"Okay, let's find out what happened between them."

Stella approached. "Hello, guys. I can hear the two of you fighting again. Someone who doesn't know any better might think the two of you were married."

"Whose side are you on?" Iris asked.

Stella chuckled. "You guys goofed."

"How?" I asked.

"There's no car in the garage and Harvey Shulman owns a car"

"Aw shit! We got on about the dog and I forgot to check," I said.

"What happened to the dog?" Stella asked.

"He's in jail, downstairs. Gabe booked him on vagrancy."

"Taking the dog home, Gabe?" Stella asked.

"I'm not sure."

"Well, dogs make good company. Doesn't anyone want him?"

"I have a feeling the answer might be no. We'll find out soon. Iris and I are going to see the only immediate relative, a younger brother. From what Iris said, I have a feeling all he wants is some money that the missing Mr. Shulman owes him. While we look into Melville Shulman, I'll put out an APB on the car."

Stella put her report into my hands. "My advice, you two, is to stop fighting and learn to accept. It makes for a reasonable life. Not perfect, mind you, but reasonable." She chuckled again as she walked away.

Iris looked at me. "She's right. Let's call a truce."

"I'm with you."

"Good. Go find your walker and let's go."

"*Oy veh!*" I muttered.

I KNOCKED ON Melville Shulman's door. A tall, thin, cantankerous-looking man whose smile was upside down, opened the door. We showed him our badges and, before I had a chance to say anything, Melville blurted, "What more do you want?"

"Mr. Shulman, I'm Detective Garshowitz and this is my partner, Detective Forester. We're investigating your brother's disappearance. There's an indication of foul play. We do need to talk to you. If you please, sir, let's go inside so we can get our information. This won't take long."

There appeared to be a battle going on inside Melville's head and, from the look of his eyes, I wasn't sure which side would win. Finally Melville stepped aside. His reverse smile got bigger. "Make it quick. I don't have anything good to say about him. Everyone knows he and I don't talk. He cheated me out of my share of the company when he wound it down and that makes him a crook in my eyes. And a bastard! Brother or not, he should rot in hell."

I looked at Iris and she made a face. We followed Melville Shulman into the living room. I sat on the couch. Melville sat opposite me, while Iris stood, just in case Melville's anger went from words to deeds. Looking at Melville Shulman, I didn't think he was a fighter, even if he was thin and wiry.

I pulled out my notebook. "When was the last time you saw your brother?"

"Do you think he's dead?"

"We don't know. We've checked all the hospitals and he's not in any of them. When did you last see him?"

"Over two weeks ago. We had a fight."

"Fight?"

"Words. I demanded my money."

"Why the confrontation?"

"He stole my money, that's why. That son of a bitch stole my money."

"Why didn't you sue him?" Iris asked.

Melville gave Iris a dirty look. "I tried, but my lawyer said I had no case."

"I don't understand. Why not?"

"Don't you know anything?" He was shouting now.

"Sir, we're trying to determine if there was a crime, and, at the same time, learn something about your brother. Why couldn't you sue him?"

"I wasn't his partner. We shared the responsibilities, me more than him. When he got sick, the ungrateful bastard, I kept the company going. And when he sold everything, I got nothing!" He rose to his feet. "Over twenty years with him. Twenty years! He owed me. I worked harder than him. I worked outside. Do you know what it's like to work in the cold? You freeze your ass. He was the inside man, the so-called brains. He wore a shirt and tie. I wore coveralls and dirt. He could have made me an inside man. But he didn't. Big man, my brother! Anyway, what difference is it if I didn't put money into his fuckin' company? I worked long hours and got nothing for it. He got it all." Melville towered over me, his anger all-consuming. Spittle foamed at the side of his mouth and his face turned red.

"We're you paid for your work?"

"Paid? Yeah, peanuts! The value was in the company's equity. I was entitled to a part. Any more questions?" he demanded. "Go find him and get me my money."

"Do you own a car?" Mr. Shulman?"

"A car? No, I don't own a car. When my brother sold everything, he never renewed the lease on my car. No, I don't own a car?"

I rose to my feet. "Do you have any idea who might want to harm your brother?"

Melville looked at me in disgust. "Don't play that stupid game with me. I didn't do anything to my brother except curse the day he was born. I'm the last one who wants him dead. I want my money. I want it now. I'm not a well person either, you know." He stalked toward the front door and we followed.

"You had a job for twenty years, Mr. Shulman," Iris said.

He glared at Iris, the colour on his face deepening. "A job! I didn't have a job. I had a position. I made that company. Without me, he had nothing."

"His dog, Mr. Shulman," Iris asked. "Do you want to take care of him?"

"No!" Without another word he slammed the door behind us.

"Pleasant fellow," I said.

"For a minute there, I thought he was going to slug you." She reached into her bag and retrieved a photograph of Melville Shulman. "I had him pegged as a nice, quiet guy who was ornery and lonely."

"Isn't that a bit of a contradiction?"

"Yep. That's what men are – a contradiction. Also, he was never married."

I stared at the photograph. "How do you know that?"

"When I looked through his brother's photograph albums, there were none of Melville getting married, just Harvey. But pictures can be deceiving."

"How'd you know it was Melville in the photos?"

"He was the best man. Some of the other shots had him under the tent and I figured that's a place of honour."

"It's called a *chupa*."

Iris looked at me, not sure I was making with the mouth again. I smiled to show my sincerity. "The tent's called a *chupa*. It's the roof that symbolizes many things to those being married in the Jewish faith."

She nodded. "Okay. Anyway, I was right, right?"

I climbed into the car without answering. I had forgotten to check the photo albums and Iris knew it. The goddamn pain in my knees was screwing up my thinking.

THAT NIGHT I took Mystic home with me. The dog seemed resigned to my authority because he made no effort to run away. He also appeared to be well trained. God, he looked sad. On the way home, I had dropped into Wal-Mart and bought a brush, dog food and a bowl. I pulled a large Hudson Bay blanket out of the closet and placed it on the kitchen floor for him to lie on. After I made myself dinner, I went into the den and switched on the television. My routine hardly varied.

Being a widower has its bad moments; coming home to an empty house was the worst. Having nothing to do after dinner ranked second. I watched the dog lying in the middle of the floor and wondered what I was going to do with him. Mystic faced the window, head between his paws, eyes glued on the darkness beyond the pane, never making a sound. Heaving a sigh I was sure could be heard outside my apartment, I got to my feet and retrieved the brush. "Come here, Mystic," I called softly.

The animal turned his head and stared at me for a second, then returned to his previous pose.

"Come here, Mystic," I tried again.

The dog looked at me again, then slowly rose to his feet and placed his head between my legs.

"Talking's good for the soul," I said. "Want to talk?" Mystic's woeful eyes held mine as his tongue kept beat with his heart. I gently stroked the brush over his head and Mystic closed his eyes and mouth. Using small, gentle strokes, I worked the brush over his back and down his side. The eyes stayed close, but the tongue flipped out and played its heartfelt tune. "What am I going to do with you? I don't even know if my lease allows me to have a pet. Mind you, I've seen a few cats around."

Mystic licked my face.

"Thanks, it's been years since anyone kissed me. Ever been in love, Mystic? It's like nothing you'll ever experience. You can tell when a person's in love – the kiss gives it away. I know." I continued to drag the brush across Mystic's back. "Yes, it's the kiss, soft and moist. My wife's were like that. When her lips became dry and hard, I should have noticed. But I was too busy to see the change. Too busy with what? I can't even remember why I was too busy. To lose a love is to lose the will to live sometimes. I can tell you loved your master, and he loved you but not his brother. Any ideas where your master might be?"

Mystic raised his head and stared into my face, but didn't make a sound.

"Got nothing to say? Well, you think about it." I kept on with my grooming. "Should have gotten a dog years ago. Would have kept Edith company when I wasn't around. Do you know that loneliness is a killer? Too much time to think." After twenty minutes, I put the brush down and Mystic gave me another lick. Obviously the dog's owner had been gentle. Not the picture Melville gave. Mystic flopped on the floor by my feet and closed his eyes. "Whenever you feel like it, you can talk to me," I said. "You and me have a lot in common." Mystic looked at me a second, then closed his eyes. His breathing became regular and I figured he'd fallen asleep. "What do you know?" I whispered. "What do you know?" I got up slowly. The movement shot pain behind my knees. I hobbled to the couch and took off my clothes. It was going to be another toss and turn night. Before getting into bed, I took two Tylenol 3s and made a note to call my doctor. The pain was getting worse.

THE NEXT DAY, I was in before Iris and received a report that the missing car had been found in a plaza parking lot in the east end, miles from Harvey Shulman's house. It had been towed away by one of the city's friendly tow trucks that prowled the streets lifting cars from plaza parking lots after the 2:00 a.m. deadline and impounding them for fees that made the average motorist choke. A few minutes later, Iris walked in. She was wearing a black windbreaker with a belt and black slacks. She knew how to dress. She also looked good enough to eat. Figuratively speaking, that is. "Let's go," I said, "I got a report the car's at a pound."

I drove. I had purchased a tensor bandage at Shoppers Drugs and tied it around my left knee. The druggist said it would reduce the swelling. I had had trouble getting my foot into my shoe that morning.

"I checked with the Department of Transportation and Melville Shulman does not own a car. I also got his bank records and he has enough money stashed away to buy a dozen cars, and for cash. So why no car?" Iris asked.

"For the most obvious reason – to feel his pain. Every time he needs a car and knows he hasn't got one, it fuels his hate."

"Something else's been bothering me. The dog," Iris said. "Why didn't the dog attack the person who must have been struggling with his master?"

"I don't think the dog was in the room."

"He was when we got there."

"I know."

"Any ideas?"

"I think the dog was downstairs during the fight and let in after it was finished. Harvey Shulman let someone into the house and they went upstairs. The fact that they went upstairs interests me."

"Why don't you figure someone broke in?"

"You don't take a stranger into your bedroom. Also, the desk in that room had an assortment of business papers stacked on top. Whoever he took up there had to do with his business. Nothing else in that room was connected to his business."

"Why not a woman? There was a bed in there and, although he's sixty, he's not necessarily sexually dead. Are you?"

I laughed, a bit uncomfortably. "That information is on a need-to-know basis. How interested are you?"

Iris grinned. "Listen, Gabe. Girls my age don't go to bed with guys old enough to be their grandfather."

"I'm not that old."

Iris chuckled. "You are to me. Let's get back to business, old man. Why not a woman?"

I offered an exaggerated sigh. "You think about it and tell me."

We drove a few more blocks. "You're right," she said. No food, nothing to show he was entertaining, and the bed was made. Messed up, but made. More than likely the messing-up was thanks to the dog. You're right. If he had a woman, there would have been a sense of preparation and there wasn't. Most guys don't bring hookers home. The last thing they want is to have the hooker know who they are and where they live. It can get complicated. How about same sex?"

"Remote. Remember he was married for over thirty-eight years."

"Okay, not likely. His brother?"

"Good possibility, but they don't talk to each other unless it's through a lawyer. There might be other people who had grievances against him. After we dig some more, we'll know better. In the meantime, we have his car and we'll see what that reveals." We pulled up to the car pound used by the towing service and I recognized the place from a previous visit. "This might be awkward," I said. "The owner doesn't like me."

"You've had a run-in with him?"

"You could say that."

"What about?"

I made a face. "Greg and I were on a stake-out about three in the morning. It was raining. We were parked in this little strip plaza for hours. Our suspect was across the street in an office building. Greg had gone for some coffee and I had to take a leak. I left the car and hurried into an alley. When I got back, a tow truck was pulling my car out of the plaza. I yelled at him to stop as he approached me. The driver gave me the finger and laughed. I was so mad I picked up a metal garbage pail by the curb and heaved it into his windshield. When he stormed out at me, I showed him my badge and made him uncouple my car. My suspect was leaving the building at that moment and drove away before I could follow. I was so pissed off I arrested the driver of the truck and impounded the vehicle. Then I made sure the owner paid a hefty bill before it was released. The asshole was pulling cars off plaza strips that had No Parking after 2:00 a.m. signs and working the car owners for big bucks to get their cars back. The owner of the towing company was fit to be tied when it was all over."

"You busted the guy's windshield? You can't do that. What happened to you?"

I grinned. "Your uncle smoothed out the ruffled feathers; Greg's a good guy. I got a reprimand. You and he don't talk. How come?"

"Personal."

"I see. Well, if ever you want to make it impersonal, I'm a good listener. Ask Mystic. Anyway, this took place about eight years ago. If the owner recognizes me, we'll be in for some trouble."

"You're so exciting to be with," Iris said, smiling. "Come on, I'll protect you."

I rolled my eyes and left the car.

Inside the dingy office sat big Charlie G. The G was for a Polish name that no one could pronounce. I entered first. Charlie was working on some papers on his desk. He looked up and recognized me in an instant. His face turned redder than the inside of a watermelon. In fact, with all the pockmarks on his face, a watermelon was a good description. He got to his feet so fast his chair fell backwards with a thud and ended up sideways at his feet. "What the fuck do you want?"

"It's nice to see you, too," I said. "I'm here about the 1998 green

Toyota Camry that your friendly driver picked up abandoned in a plaza on Danforth Avenue near Main."

"That'll cost you three hundred bucks. It was a legit job." He stood in front of me, his eyes boring into my face, his smirk indicating he was enjoying himself. "No money, no car."

"This is police business."

He grinned, his bad breath closing the gap between us. "No money, no car," he repeated slowly. "I'm an honest dealer and you can't deny me what is mine. No car."

"Can we look at it?" Iris asked.

Charlie G noticed Iris for the first time, standing by the door. His grin turned into a leer. "Hello, sweetie," he said. "You with the bozo?"

I cringed. Charlie G had just made a big mistake.

"We'll get you your money," she said. "Right now we want to look at the car just to make sure it's the one we're looking for. Be nice and co-operate."

"You can't go in it. Not until I get paid."

"Just want to look."

He walked past me and stood in front of Iris. I turned to watch. She had been talking between clenched teeth, but she was smiling.

"Okay, sweetie, for you anything. Maybe we could have dinner sometime?"

Iris still smiled. Charlie G should be looking at her eyes, not her breasts, I thought.

Charlie G left the office and headed for the pound in back. Iris was right behind him, and I behind her. I could tell that Iris was going to explode lava if our escort said 'sweetie' one more time. Charlie G stopped in front of a car and pointed. His eyes were on Iris, his thoughts doubtless in the gutter. I walked around the vehicle and peered into the windows. Iris kept her eye on Charlie G. When I was finished, I approached him. "Where are the original tires?"

"What d'you mean?" he said.

"You swapped the tires for baldies. Those tires on the car are so smooth they couldn't grab shit. You changed the tires. No one drives on anything that bald. So, where're the original tires? We need them."

Charlie G's look turned ugly. "What you see is what you get."

"I think not. You're impeding an investigation. I want the originals and I want the keys. This car is being impounded by the police."

"Up yours."

"Trouble, boss?"

Charlie G's clone, Big and Ugly, had appeared. "Police business. Back off," I said.

"You a cop?" Big and Ugly snorted. "Coulda fooled me. Boy, you got me scared." He turned to Charlie G. "Want me to toss them out?"

"Him. Leave the little lady for me."

"I'm also a cop," Iris said, approaching Big and Ugly. "Want to toss me out?"

His grin widened, showing no bottom teeth in front. "The boss wants to toss you." He laughed at his supposed joke, pushed her aside and came for me.

Iris swung a fist into his kidney. Big and Ugly's face went red, his mouth opened as the oxygen gushed from between his lips and he let go one big fart. The smell staggered Iris. She backed away. He swung around and faced her, his fists clenched. Growling like an enraged bear, he charged. Before I had a chance to interfere, Iris smoothly avoided his rush, dropped to one knee and rammed her fist into his testicles. A squeal of pain emerged from his mouth, his eyes popped and he farted again as he fell to the floor like a train falling off a trestle, his hands clutching between his legs.

"Son of a bitch!" Charlie G screamed, charging Iris. He swung his fist. Iris diverted the blow over her shoulder, grabbed his outstretched arm and threw him over her body, letting his momentum carry him over her shoulders to land on Big and Ugly's face.

I raced over and handcuffed both their hands together. "Good teamwork," I said.

Iris glared at me.

"Just kidding," I said. "I'll call headquarters and get a truck down here to take the car away. Sit down, you look tired."

"Geezus, did you smell him?"

"Smell what?" The air was still ripe. I stuck out my tongue and gagged.

AFTER FORENSICS TOOK the car away, the original tires were located and examined. We spent the day checking into Shulman's background while waiting for Forensics to give us some insight on where the car might have been. I went home that night and walked Mystic. The dog tugged on his leash, straining to go somewhere but not where I intended. I wasn't used to walking. After all, what was the point? Where do you walk when you're alone? I'd seen old men strolling in malls trying to fill time and it was a sad sight. Sitting home alone, clicking the remote on my television from channel to channel, trying to fill the void of doing nothing, was my method of hiding my loneliness. Mystic's presence was having an effect on me. He shared my loneliness and was a good listener. I didn't call the doctor either. I don't know whether the tensor bandage was responsible, but the pain seemed to have subsided. I popped a couple of Tylenol 3s throughout the day and I guess that helped. Maybe I'll call the doctor tomorrow.

The night air was not biting; street lamps illuminated the area as vehicular traffic busily passed. I sat on one of the benches outside the park by my apartment and watched life pass. Mystic sat in front of me, eyes focused on the traffic. "Ever wonder about life, Mystic? Its purpose? Why you are born, why you are alone, why you're loved by your parents? You find love, marry and make a life. Death enters and loneliness returns, but this time it's accompanied by pain. You're born, you live, you die, for what?" I looked to Mystic for an answer, but his eyes were on the passing cars. "That, too, is life. Passing by so quickly, each day an eternity, each year a breath, every neglected moment a memory that never dies. Stored one on top of the other."

Mystic turned his head and fixed his gaze on me.

"Ready to go back?" I stood, bent down and ruffled Mystic's head. "I hope my problems don't weigh on you as they do on me. I'm afraid of getting old, Mystic. I had it all and wasted it. Do you know I have a kid? Don't even know where she is. I made a mess of her life by not being there when she needed a father. I had my priorities mixed up. That's what life is all about. Priorities." My pace was slow as we made our way back to the apartment. The pain in my knees had returned. I wondered if it was the weather.

I moved Mystic's blanket from the kitchen to my bedroom. I was getting ready for bed when Mystic came over and nudged me with his nose. I wasn't sure what that meant, so I gently stroked his head. The brush I had used the day before was on my dresser. I picked it up and started brushing. Mystic's tongue beat a fast tempo, his body pushed against the brush as he absorbed each stroke with silent contentment. After a while, I told him it was time to go to bed. The dog looked at me with eyes that said thank you, then flopped onto the blanket. "You're a good dog, Mystic. You had a good master."

WHEN I SHOWED up at my desk the next day, Iris had the forensic report. "Forensics found gravel in the tire treads and the trunk had a few drops of blood and some loose earth."

"Harvey Shulman's buried somewhere," I said.

"Brilliant. Where?"

"In the ground."

"What's eating you?"

"Nothing."

"Well, get a handle on nothing and come to grips with it. Why the terse answers?"

I plopped into my seat and stared out the window trying to understand what was eating me. Iris waited for my answer, which was unlike her. "Did you see a doctor yesterday?"

"No, that's not it."

"You're a shmuck! It's the dog. He's getting to you."

"He's a good dog, Iris. He was well treated. I can tell. That tells me Harvey Shulman was a good man. Good men don't lie buried in anonymity. I think his brother's responsible in some way. I can't figure out if it was premeditated or an accident, but my gut tells me Melville Shulman's the bad guy."

"You're gut is sticking over your belt. Remember about hunches?"

"This is no itch. I know it's him."

"Then bring him in," she said.

"A waste of time. That cantankerous old SOB is enjoying the situation. Why kill someone and not profit? That's not Melville. He wants money. The question is, where does a cantankerous old man bury a sick old man?"

Iris was sitting opposite me as I gazed at the forensic report. "Close to the house. The body would be too heavy for him to lug too far. I'd say someplace not far, and close enough that a car can get to the place where he dumps the body," she said.

"Makes sense. Gravel, you said. A dirt road or a gravel pit, or north of the city where the side roads are gravel. How far is close?"

"How about a park?"

"Too public."

"I'm not so sure."

"Maybe a conservation park, just outside of Toronto. Boyd, maybe," I answered.

"Roads are closed at night. They have barriers blocking the entrance. No, wrong kind of park."

"We can sit here all day and not come up with the right answer. I'll go see Harvey Shulman's lawyer, you see his doctor. Find out what blood type he is. In the meantime, let's figure out where Melville buried his brother."

Iris went to Dr. Gerry Isenberg, Harvey Shulman's doctor, while I went to Sheldon Berg, his lawyer. At the end of the day, we met at headquarters and compared notes.

"The doctor wouldn't say too much about Harvey Shulman's medical history, but he did tell me that what he was being treated for was hereditary and both brothers had similar health problems," Iris said. "And the blood in the trunk is his type."

"Are you saying Melville has the same condition?"

"He treats them both. Melville never had a heart attack. It affects people differently."

"Did the doctor tell you when he was last there for an examination?" I asked.

"Yes. A few days before he disappeared."

"And?"

"He said he was fine, considering."

"Considering what? Doesn't he realize we're trying to help?"

"Yes. He wasn't being difficult, Gabe. He didn't know if Mr. Shulman would want his medical records revealed. Harvey also had a thing about his brother and didn't want his brother to know anything about his health. As I was leaving, the doctor handed me a brochure on congestive heart failure. One of the symptoms is dizziness and light-headedness from low blood pressure."

"That's interesting."

"What did you find?" Iris asked.

I smiled. "A whole bunch. Harvey started the company. After three years he offered Melville an equal share. He wanted the book value at the time but Melville wanted to pay what Harvey started with. Start-up was $10,000. By this time, the company was worth about $25,000. So Harvey wanted $12,500, but Melville wanted to pay $5,000. They couldn't come to terms, so Harvey withdrew the offer and began paying him a salary equal to what he was paying himself and that was how the company existed for the next twenty-four years. When Harvey had a heart attack five years ago, he gave Melville signing power. He was away for two months. When he came back, he found that Melville had taken twice his normal pay. When Harvey asked why, Melville claimed he was doing the work of two and was therefore entitled to twice the wages. A few months later, Harvey sold the company for $500,000 and gave his brother the difference between what he had taken from a $50,000 severance pay. That started the final argument. Apparently they argued about everything."

"Who was right?"

"Sometimes one, sometimes the other. The lawyer became the referee. He said Harvey was a good man, but when it came to his brother, he was a different person."

"Sounds like Melville's a *putz*," Iris said.

"Not according to Melville."

"He could have had $250,000 if he had paid his brother $7,500 more than he offered. That's a *putz*!"

"The question is, is that reason enough to kill his brother?"

"Are you referring to the $50,000 or the $250,000?" Iris said. "Who knows what someone with that kind of tunnel vision would do? I'd say it's not impossible."

"You're right, it's not impossible. Let's talk to Melville Shulman again."

WITHOUT A BODY, the evidence indicated too many options. Blood on a table, spots on the floor, missing carpet, blood in the trunk of a car … It would appear a violent crime had been committed and yet, nothing was missing from the house as near as they could tell, no break and enter and no body. Kidnapping was a possibility, but nobody was making any demands. Harvey Shulman didn't appear to have any real enemies, except his brother, and although they'd been known to argue, the arguments were never violent. Loud, but not physical. The problem was, was Harvey dead? Had he injured himself? Did he take himself to a hospital and lose his memory? If so, why was the car found where it was?

Melville let us into his apartment and was his usual charming self as we sat in his living room. "Why are you badgering me? Am I being accused of something?"

"No, Mr. Shulman," I answered. "We're trying to figure out what happened to your brother. You are his only living relative. We're trying to understand what your brother was like and whether his disappearance was by choice or by force."

"Do you think he's dead?"

"You've asked me that before. At this point, I can't say."

"If he's not dead, what do you want from me? He owes me money. If he pays, I don't care what happens to him. If he's dead, I won't get my money. I'm not in his will."

"How do you know?"

"I am not a fool, Detective. Why would my brother put me in his will? Why give me money after his death if he won't give it to me before? I'll tell you this, if you can't find his body, no one gets his money for seven years. Not even the charities he more than likely left it to. He even left money to the dog. The dog! Me, nothing. As his only living relative, I'll claim a share. I'll make it so tough that the charities will compromise. By then the damn dog will be dead. They'll give me his share. As long as the body's not found, I'll get my money – eventually."

"How do you know the dog's in the will?" I asked.

"My brother told me!" he shouted, glaring at me like I was stupid. "If I killed him, it's for damn sure you're too stupid to catch me."

"Are you challenging me, Mr. Shulman?"

Melville stood up, smirking. "No. I'm telling you my brother cheated me out of my share of the company. I'm entitled to half of what he got when he sold it. He used his heart attack as an excuse. You think I did something? Prove it. Find his goddamn body." For the first time, a look of sheer pleasure crossed Melville Shulman's face. "If you can. If not, leave me alone."

"I'll find the body if there is one, Mr. Shulman," I said.

"No you won't," he said in a quiet voice, still grinning. "You'll walk all over it, but never find it." As he led us to the front door, he never stopped grinning.

Iris and I left his apartment knowing the answer to the big question. The arrogant son of a bitch had done it.

FOR THREE DAYS, Iris and I went over every lead, but nothing new turned up. Melville Shulman did his brother in, of that we were sure. Melville must have come to Harvey's house for a showdown, they went upstairs to where Harvey kept his business papers and argued. Maybe Melville pushed him, Harvey lost his balance, fell and struck his head and died. An accident? Melville panicked or maybe he killed him deliberately and covered up what he'd done by burying the body. He didn't have a car so he didn't have to go back and get it. He dumped his brother's car and went home afterwards. It sounded a bit far fetched, but that was our conclusion. We were convinced he was responsible for Harvey's death, even though we didn't have a body. What we didn't know was whether it was accidental or deliberate. That old man was making an ass of us.

I finally went back to my doctor. Now he thought I might have a torn meniscus. A torn what? Soft tissue behind the knee. It has a tendency to weaken in older, overweight people. So how did I tear it? Something as simple as getting off a chair or standing from a crouched position. Any number of ways. He asked if I had trouble tying my shoelaces. I said no. He seemed surprised. I wear loafers, I said. Boy would he make a terrible cop. He had arranged an MRI. I had to wait four months or go to the States. I called my brother and told him my problem. He let me know how much it would cost if I went to Buffalo. I decided to wait the distance. The tensor bandage stopped working. I discovered that pain can be very personal.

It snowed again. December in Toronto this year was going to be difficult for the old, a pleasure for the sports-minded and a pain in the ass for me and my knees. On the third day, I came home to Mystic and asked him the sixty-four-thousand-dollar question. "What happened?

You were there. Say something." That was when I realized that Mystic had not barked since the first day. Hadn't made a sound since being led away from the house. When we went walking, he always strained at the leash, but was obedient to my commands. Silent obedience. Even dogs feel pain, I thought.

Other cases were taking our time away from the Shulman case. Time seemed to be working in favour of Melville. It was no secret among the cops at the precinct that I wanted to solve the disappearance. It was also no secret that I seemed to be less confrontational. That's what Iris called me. I never figured I was confrontational. She referred to my change as "Mysticpower."

HOLLOWAY APPROACHED IRIS sitting at her desk. "Where's Gabe?"

"He had an errand."

Holloway sat opposite her. "Uh, I was wondering if everything is okay?"

"Sure. Why wouldn't it be?" She looked down at her hands.

"Where is he?"

She raised her head. "Took Mystic to be groomed. Only appointment he could get."

"I see. How, uh, how are you getting along?"

"Fine. Why wouldn't we?"

"He's a good man, Iris. And you're a good cop. You know you're his daughter's age."

"No, I didn't know. Is that why you teamed us?"

"That, and another reason. I wanted to make sure you learned from the best." He paused. "About your father and me . . ."

"I've decided not to be involved. It's between you two. I'm discovering that not everything is as it seems."

"I'm glad. There's something else. There's something the matter with Gabe, isn't there?"

"What do you mean?"

"The way he walks. He has a problem. A serious problem that he hasn't told me about. Should I be concerned?"

"No."

"That's it? No."

"It's under control. He's seeing someone."

He looked at her, his face showing he was sympathetic. "He's a good friend, you know that. You'll keep me in touch if I should be concerned, won't you?"

"It's under control."

"I heard you the first time."

"Uncle Greg . . . Uh, I can call you that, can't I?"

Greg smiled and leaned forward. "Only if no one else is listening. I'd like that."

Iris nodded. "About Gabe . . . I like him, too. I like him a lot. He's a good guy as well as a good cop. He doesn't fool me with his sexist talk. He's lonely and I feel for him."

"He's older than your father."

Iris shook her head. "No, not that way. I think I can fill some of that loneliness by being his friend. I want to be partners until he retires. But don't tell him I said that."

Greg stood. "I think you two are made for each other. It's a deal," he said. "I'll tell you something. He's said the same thing."

IRIS AND I were busy. We had our hands full with what looked like a lovers' spat that ended in murder. The suspect was hiding out in the city, we figured, and we were hunting down the leads. That meant a lot of walking. When the knees are concerned, the simple act of walking becomes tantamount to climbing a mountain. I was having trouble and still had three months before my MRI appointment. My doctor suspected arthritis, but it could also be a torn meniscus. I was getting to learn a lot about degenerative illness. One day, Iris greeted me with some good news.

"Your appointment for an MRI has been bumped to one o'clock in the morning at another hospital," she said.

"How come?"

"I was able to pull some strings."

"Who do you know that has that kind of influence?"

"My ex."

"Really. What's he do?"

"He's a sports doctor. I had dinner with him last night and this morning he called with the appointment."

"You just had dinner with him?"

"Yes, just dinner."

"Did you have to give away the family jewels?"

"They aren't jewels any more."

"Thank him for me," I said.

"He got his reward."

FOUR MONTHS LATER, Holloway called us into his office. "Melville Shulman has had a heart attack. He's asked for you. He's at General Hospital."

I had trouble holding back my smile. "So maybe we finally hear what happened," I said.

At the hospital, we met Dr. Isenberg leaving Melville's room. He offered us a tired smile.

"Not too long."

"What happened?" Iris asked.

"Threw a tantrum with his brother's lawyer. He went ballistic."

We went into the room. Melville had more machines pinging than a video arcade; tubes in his nose, I.V. in his arms, wires running from one machine or another and he was breathing like a steam engine. He looked terrible. As we stood over him, his eyes opened.

"Want to find my brother?" he wheezed.

"Sure," I said.

Melville closed his eyes and his lips moved, but I couldn't hear anything. "What?"

Melville forced his eyes open. "Fuck you!"

The machines hit high notes and the heart monitor flattened out. The nurse ran in and told us to leave. We did. A few minutes later, Dr. Isenberg rushed in.

"What a stubborn bastard," I said to Iris.

"When it came to his brother, he had total tunnel vision. They both did." She shook her head. "Am I glad I have no brothers and sisters."

The doctor came out.

"What's the verdict, doc?" I asked.

"We lost him. Sorry, there was nothing I could do." He continued down the hall.

"It looks like he took the secret to the grave with him," Iris said.

BEFORE RETURNING TO headquarters, we drove over to the lawyer's office to find out what had triggered Melville's tantrum. Mr. Berg greeted us in the foyer and walked us into his office.

"A few minutes ago, Melville Shulman died at General Hospital," I said.

"That's unfortunate, but I'm not sorry. I've never liked him. What is it you want to know?"

"You and he had an argument, I understand."

"What? No, not at all! He asked me about Harvey's will. I knew I could prevent him from knowing for a while, but I wanted him to know. It wasn't what he expected."

"What did it say?" Iris asked.

"Well, Harvey left money for the dog, an allowance, so to speak, in the event that he died before the dog did, to be used by whoever would take care of him until he died."

"Really? How much?" I asked.

"Five thousand a year for ten years. The dog being about eight, Harvey estimated the dog might live to about eighteen. Any money not spent on the dog from the allowance would go to the person who cared for him. I was to invest fifty thousand and give five out every year. With interest there should be a tidy sum left over for the caregiver."

I saw the look Iris gave me and shook my head to say nothing. "And the rest?"

"A hundred thousand to the Heart and Stroke Foundation because of his condition and a hundred thousand to the Canadian Cancer Society because of his wife. The rest, about a million dollars after selling his assets would go to Melville."

"No shit!" I exclaimed.

Berg smiled. "No shit. Unfortunately, since we don't have a body, he would have to wait at least seven years to collect, or until such time as there was definite evidence that Harvey Shulman was dead. That was when he blew a gasket."

I felt my mouth drop.

"Yep," Iris said. "I call that justice."

BACK AT HEADQUARTERS, Iris showed me a small article from the *Toronto Star*.

DOG TRACKS OWNER TO GRAVE

A border collie has tracked down his former owner's grave despite never having been there before. The dog escaped from his new owner's home more than six kilometres from where his former owner was buried, crossing busy roads before lying down on the grave of his 73-year-old previous owner.

"Do you have any idea what you're implying? Do you realize how big Toronto is?"

"No! Tell me. No, never mind. Let me tell you."

"Where?"

"Remember Melville said, 'You'll walk all over him, but never find him'?"

I thought a minute. "Okay. Let's say a park. Which one? The city has a thousand parks."

"One that has a road into it. Remember what we're dealing with here. Melville wasn't strong enough to carry something as heavy as a body very far; a big park with a road, and my guess probably not too far from Harvey's house."

"Why not High Park?"

Iris shook her head. "Too far. That bastard was cunning. He dumped the car in the east part of the city and close to downtown. That's a false clue. From the Danforth he hopped a subway home. He's already dumped the body and that means nearby. When you think about it, that leaves only two. Earl Bales or G. Ross Lord. I say G. Ross Lord Park. Earl Bales has a short road off Bathurst. It's in a residential area. The grounds are too open. It used to be a golf course, rolling hills and flat, very few trees. Now G. Ross Lord is a different kind of park, a conservation park, several roads, twists and turns, and trees, lots of trees and thick bushes, and lots of ravines. There's a dozen ways to get into the park on foot, but only one by car. Across from the Dufferin entrance are a lot of parking spaces from the commercial businesses – even a huge food store with a massive parking lot and it's open until midnight. A car sitting there late would not be suspicious. Drive into the park, dump the body somewhere, drive out, park the car, return on foot, bury the body, then back to the car and home. Get rid of the tools, drive it away from the area and come back by public transit. G. Ross Lord Park is where I figure the body is. Now, could Mystic locate it?"

I stood, grinning. "My dog can do anything,"

"Your dog?"

"Yes, my dog. And I don't want the money. It can go to the Humane Society."

WE DROVE TO my apartment, got Mystic, went to Iris's and then to G. Ross Lord Park, to a parking section near the trees. Iris put on her running shoes. Mystic sat down while I unhooked the leash. Free of restraint, Mystic looked at me but made no effort to leave. "Go find Harvey," I said. Mystic turned his head and looked at the park. "Go find Harvey," I said more loudly. Mystic rose to his feet and glanced at me and then out at the park. "Go!"

And he went.

Iris took off after the dog at a run.

I walked. I'd been taking an anti-inflammatory pill. It made a world of difference. I still had pain but nowhere near the intensity. I was told to get used to it. My walking was steadier and not so exaggerated. At home, I used a cane though. I never brought it to work.

Iris and Mystic were gone from sight within seconds. Down a hill or around a bend, I didn't know. I stuck to the road. Then I heard Mystic barking. I followed the sound into the trees. It took me a while to get there, and when I did, I saw Mystic digging away like mad. Iris was panting and grinning like a Cheshire cat. "What do you think?" she said.

Mystic barked.

"Harvey's here."

And he was.

HARVEY SHULMAN WAS buried ceremoniously next to his brother Melville. It seemed ironic that the two who had never gotten along in life should be buried on the same day, side by side. We stayed until both graves were covered and everyone had left. Mystic sat obediently beside me and watched it all. Dogs aren't stupid; Mystic had to sense what was happening. I didn't even have him on a leash – didn't need it. It wasn't that I was his owner as much as Mystic had agreed to be my dog. Iris and I headed for the car when I realized that Mystic wasn't beside me. I turned to see where he was and saw him doing his business on Melville's grave.

Iris laughed. "Did you bring a bag?"

"For what?" I answered as I continued to the car. "You know, what just happened was illegal."

"That's why I asked if you had a plastic bag," Iris answered.

"No. I don't mean that." I gestured at the grave. "What just happened was double jeopardy. You can't punish a criminal twice for the same crime."

Mystic ran ahead of them, barking.

"Wanna bet?" Iris said, laughing.

I smiled. I was feeling good. All the bad in my life was behind me. I had a good partner and a good dog. It had been a long time coming. I opened the door to my car and Mystic bounded in. Iris got into the passenger side and I climbed in behind the wheel.

"Remember," Iris said calmly, "you must turn the key clockwise for the car to start."

I snorted. "Don't you ever let up?"

"In your case, never. Let's go, old man. Another day, another case."

Section Three:

3

Stories About People

THE OPEN DRAPES revealed the moon hovering in the corner of our bedroom window, its full face beaming inside as if to see if Marilyn and I had gone to bed. The moon that had discreetly witnessed our lovemaking reflected, not the brightness of Marilyn's presence, but an ominous illumination of the emptiness of nights yet to come. I sat alone on the couch, staring at the floor, waiting for the telephone to ring.

Our large bedroom had a spacious, high ceiling, combining bedroom and sitting room furniture; a section of the house away from the activities from the rest of the household. A room of memories. Several bookcases were strategically placed in both rooms, every shelf filled with books and on each shelf photographs were on display; photographs that showed a man and a woman smiling, their eyes shining with the joy of each other's presence and always holding hands, their fingers interlocked.

But now, the house felt empty, a feeling of heaviness hung in the air. I sensed Marilyn's presence, but knew I was alone for she was in the hospital undergoing surgery to stop the spread of cancer. I had asked to stay, but the doctor told me I should go home. "We'll call you," he said. "Staying here won't be good for you." I had recently suffered a heart attack.

Reluctantly, my three children and I went home. Each of us had gone to our own rooms, wanting to be alone. The only sound was of the wind tapping on the glass, a sound that would normally lull Marilyn and me to sleep. But this was not a normal night.

I focused my eyes on the telephone, waiting for it to ring. I placed my hands over my face and breathed slowly into my dry palms. I could hear her voice in my head, the sound of her laughter and I glanced quickly about the room half hoping she was there, that what had taken place was a bad dream. Restlessly, I paced the room, stopping at the mantel over the fireplace where Marilyn had displayed several photographs. Each told a story.

I picked one up. We were in the country. I had to smile, recalling the reason we were there. While driving to see a client, I had heard on the radio the station promoting a poetry contest for St. Valentine's Day; the grand winner would receive an all-expense paid weekend for two at a resort in Muskoka, Ontario's prime cottage country. The runners-up would get boxes of truffles. The contest called for entrants to compose an original poem about love, the winning selections to be read the night before St. Valentines Day.

I decided to enter the contest, hoping to win a box of truffles. Realizing the odds of my even being a runner-up were slim, I didn't tell Marilyn what I intended to do. After all, if my entry was not selected, I could buy her something at the last minute and my whim would remain my secret.

For several days, I agonized over the poem, writing and rewriting until I was sorry I'd even started it. It would have been easier to buy a box of truffles than to try and win a prize in a contest in which God knows how many poems would be entered. Finally satisfied with my efforts, I faxed the poem to the radio station and waited for the night of the program.

On the night the winners were to be announced, I was having difficulty keeping awake. The readings of the winning poems were to start at 11 p.m. but, long before that, I was falling asleep. While Marilyn, my two daughters and my son watched television, I dozed on the couch.

"Why don't you go to bed, dear?" Marilyn said.

"Was I snoring?"

"That's one way of putting it."

I pushed myself to my feet and glanced at my watch. It was 9:03. "Good night," I said and trudged up the stairs to our bedroom. I set my alarm clock for 10:55, intending to sneak into the basement to listen to the program. My family rarely went to bed before midnight and I felt sure they would be unaware of what I was doing. It was possible to make it from my bedroom to the basement without them catching on I was there. I undressed, climbed into bed and fell asleep before my head hit the pillow.

When the alarm went off, I sprang from the bed and headed for the stairs without putting on my robe. Just as I made it to the bottom of the stairs, I met Marilyn coming up to check on me.

"Where're you going?" Marilyn asked, as I tried to pass her.

"Downstairs. I forgot something."

"What?"

"Something."

Marilyn stared at me curiously.

I glanced at my watch; it was 11:05. I panicked. "I'll tell you later," I said. I rushed to the basement door before she could utter another word, opened it and flew down the steps. I scrambled around the furniture to the radio which I had not used for months and tuned in the station.

Music was playing.

It was now 11:10.

I had missed part of the program.

The music ended and the announcer went into his patter. The volume from the radio began to warble and the announcer's voice faded. I fiddled with the dial, trying to regain the sound, but I could only catch the odd word. He was reading a poem. They were not my words. Again music played and the full volume returned for a few minutes, only to fade again. I strained to hear what the announcer was saying but the volume became inaudible. The situation turned critical. It was now 11:25 and the radio had become dumb with silence. I dropped to my hands and knees, placed my ear against the speaker and faintly heard the announcer reading another poem. Again, the announcer's voice disappeared.

Marilyn called. "Hon, can you come upstairs?" There was a short pause before she added, "Please."

I didn't answer. I was concentrating on the words coming from the silent radio.

"Dear. Come upstairs right now."

In all our years of marriage, I could not remember her being so demanding, but I was unable to leave the radio for fear I would miss the announcer reading my poem. "I can't come up now. Give me a minute. I have to listen to the radio," I shouted back.

Marilyn called again. "Did you hear me? The police are here!"

"Who?"

"The police are here," she repeated, emphasizing each word.

I willed the radio to stop warbling, but it refused to cooperate. I gave the radio a dirty look, got to my feet and raced up the stairs, flew through the door and stopped before two tall, well-built policemen. They looked down at me with their stern, official faces. I felt small even though I am six foot-three and weigh three hundred pounds.

Perspiration leaked from my forehead and droplets of moisture dripped from my neck down my chest. Gazing up at them in my baby-blue pyjamas and bare feet, my hair in a state of uncombed shock, I wished I could disappear. "Yes, can I help you?" I said, with as much calm as I could muster.

"Dear," Marilyn cooed, "they're here in response to the burglar alarm you set off."

"What burglar alarm? We don't have any burglar system. They're coming tomorrow."

"The security company came a day early," Marilyn said, her face flushed with embarrassment. "They were in the neighbourhood to wire another home, so they decided to do ours – but forgot a cut-off switch. They told me the system was activated and not to go into the basement until they returned tomorrow. They said opening the door would set it off, triggering a response at the police station that was monitoring this area."

My mouth dropped. I looked at my watch. "I don't believe this," I mumbled. "Officers," I said to the policemen, trying to look professional in my night attire, "obviously, I live here, otherwise why am I in pajamas? I'm sorry about the alarm, but as you just heard, I wasn't informed that the security system was installed. Had I known about the alarm, I wouldn't be running around at this ungodly hour trying to listen to a radio that doesn't work."

One of the officers tried to say something but I edged towards the basement door. "This must look odd to you, but I'm caught in a ridiculous situation and I've got to go back downstairs. Please accept my apologies." As I backed away, I turned to Marilyn and pleaded. "Marilyn, tell them I'm not crazy."

Marilyn pointed her finger at me, jabbing at the air. I backed away. "Your pajamas," she mouthed. I looked down and realized the front of my pajama pants had come undone. I clutched at the opening and disappeared down the stairs, raced over to the radio, threw myself onto the floor and jammed my ear against the speaker. I could barely hear the announcer, but I caught a word here and there – words from my poem. Impatient with the radio, I scrambled to my feet and raced up the stairs two steps at a time, my fist gripping the top of my pajamas to prevent them from opening. The police officers were saying good night to Marilyn as I passed them and I could see one officer look at the other with puzzlement and concern.

Like a tank, I thudded up the steps dragging my tired body into my bedroom and turned on the clock radio. It was already tuned to the station and, with clarity of sound, I heard the announcer wish everyone a good night and express the hope that the winners would enjoy their prizes. I sank to the floor and began to moan.

"What's going on?"

I didn't answer. I just looked at her with glazed eyes, my head shaking from side to side.

"What's going on?" Marilyn repeated.

"You wouldn't believe me if I told you."

"Try me. The policeman wanted to know if he should stick around until a doctor showed up. I told him this was normal. Now start talking or I'll call them back."

I told her everything. The look on Marilyn's face changed from annoyance to utter disbelief. When I finished, she was the one shaking her head and rolling her eyes. "Did you win the truffles?"

"I don't know! I don't expect there's anyone at the switchboard at this hour, so we'll have to wait until tomorrow to find out. But the words I heard sounded like my poem and I figure maybe we did win something."

"I'm going to call now," Marilyn said. She looked up the radio station's number in the telephone book and dialed. Then she hung up. "Answering machine."

I was standing in the middle of the room, looking like the conclusion of the Rocky Horror Picture Show. "I'm going to bed. I'm too tired to think. I'll call the radio station in the morning and find out who the winners were." Then I dragged my exhausted body towards the bed. Marilyn grabbed my pyjama top and halted me. I turned, my eyes already closed, and felt her kiss on my lips.

I opened my eyes. "What's that for?"

"For the thought. Good night. I love you." She was smiling as I toppled into the bed.

The next morning, early, my office telephone rang and a sweet voice asked for me.

"Speaking."

"Congratulations. Your poem was judged number one in our contest and you won the grand prize of a weekend at Deerhurst."

I was stunned. I could not speak.

"Sir, are you there?"

"Lady," I finally answered, "if I told you what happened to me last night, you wouldn't believe it."

I found myself smiling. I replaced the photograph, the words I wrote running through my head.

LOVE WITH RESPECT

When we were young, our lives end so many years away,
We gazed at each other, pledging never to stray.
We were in love – it was too obvious not to see,
Our thoughts were one, our hearts were free.

Yet, what is love without each other's respect?
What are promises, when pursuing one disaffects?
What value are plans, if both do not support?
What good are goals if one chooses to abort?

No love lasts forever unless respect is there.
Throughout the pain of life, only respect will care.
For as time passes, bonding the two together,
Only love with respect makes the bond stronger.

And when the flame of life begins to cool its fire,
The candle in our hearts will burn ever higher.
For when all is said and done – as you would expect,
What has survived is love with respect.

I MADE MY way around the room, examining each photograph. I came to one of our younger daughter, Lori, with a mischevious smile on her face. She was the comedian in the family. The photograph had been taken on her birthday.

That morning the sun had squeezed through the partially opened drapes of our bedroom, spreading its warmth on Marilyn and me. Marilyn left our bed and made her way to the shower. I was yet unwilling to take that first brave step. A little later, the comforter was whipped off, exposing my fetal position. "Go away," I mumbled, squeezing myself into a tighter ball.

A soft hand gripped my foot and dragged me towards the edge of the bed.

"You have fifteen minutes or all you'll get is cold cereal," Marilyn said.

I opened my eyes and glared at her. "Remind me to get even later."

Marilyn smiled. "Fifteen minutes, Romeo."

As she left the bedroom, I grunted out of bed and into the bathroom. Minutes later I flew down the stairs with only seconds to spare, gave Marilyn a peck on the neck and took my seat. I was surprised to find my sixteen-year-old daughter, Lori, doing her homework at the table. My older daughter, Lisa, was already out for the day.

"Morning Shorty," I said.

Lori looked up at me and smiled. "Hi Dad."

"Kind of early for homework, isn't it?"

"I've a full day."

I smiled, opened the newspaper and immersed myself in the pages. The conversation was sporadic. I grunted a few times when Marilyn asked me a question, while Lori remained strangely silent. Occasionally, Lori stopped what she was doing, her emerald green eyes staring intently at us and, a few times, she seemed about to say something but didn't. Whatever struggle was going on inside of her showed only in her eyes.

Marilyn noticed the serious look on her face.

I had yet to surface from behind my paper barrier, my hands mechanically knew where to reach and how much to lift. The table was strewn with the remnants of what we had eaten and there was the aroma of fresh coffee; the only sound was the rustle of my newspaper. From behind my newspaper, I heard my daughter close her text books and move her chair back from the table. Glancing up, I smiled as Lori prepared to leave the kitchen.

"Why are there more pictures of Lisa than there are of me?" she asked.

I stared back, not understanding the question.

Lori turned and left the room.

I looked at Marilyn. "What happened?"

"She looked very serious," Marilyn answered.

"Are there more pictures of Lisa than of Lori?"

Marilyn shrugged her shoulders.

"How many could there be?" I added.

"I've never counted them. I don't know."

"Kids!" I exclaimed and raised the newspaper. A few minutes later, I raised my worried face. "There can't be that many more pictures of Lisa than of Lori." The puzzled look on Marilyn's face did not give me the answer I wanted to hear. I mumbled something before disappearing again, but I was having difficulty focusing on the words. "I hadn't realized there was any significant difference," I said as I closed the newspaper. "Now why would Lori ask such a question?"

Marilyn shook her head. Several minutes passed before she answered. "When Lisa was born, you were taking photographs. You hardly went anywhere without a camera. When Lori was born, you were involved in coloured slides. There must be hundreds of slides of Lori somewhere in the house that she has never seen or doesn't remember."

"Of course," I said. "When Lori leaves, we'll look for those slides. Who knows, we might find more slides of Lori than pictures of Lisa."

Later that afternoon, we went into the basement where we had stored the boxes of slides. It was not long before Marilyn located the trays of slides and for the rest of the afternoon we looked at each, separating those that highlighted Lori.

"What are you going to do?" Marilyn asked.

It was not a happy face that looked back at her.

"Are you all right?" she asked.

I nodded. "Do you know what this is all about?"

"I think so."

"It's about love. She can see the love between us, she must see the love we give to Lisa, but she can't see our love for her. I know that feeling. My mother never told me she loved me. I sensed it, I felt it, but I never heard it. There were times when I longed for her to say those words – but she never did."

"Why?"

A slow grin appeared on my face. "Old country logic, I think. My brothers and I were equal in her eyes and so she treated us equally."

"You knew she loved you."

"I know now. Then I wondered. That's what Lori's doing – wondering."

"What are you going to do?"

"Show her we love her."

"How?"

"It's her birthday in a few weeks. We'll select about one hundred slides and convert them into photographs, put them into an album and give them to her as a gift. I don't know if the album will answer her question, but at least she'll know that we cared enough to answer."

Marilyn nodded her approval.

Over the next couple of days, we secretly went through all the slides until we were satisfied with our selection. Marilyn converted them into photographs and I placed them into an album. The album was filled with good memories of the early years of our marriage and we hoped it showed how much we loved our daughter.

Early on the morning of Lori's birthday, I slipped the album into her room, letting it rest on the carpet. Attached was a birthday card with a note explaining why we had put the album together. Would she see the album as a symbol of our love? I could only hope Lori realized what it meant. I then left for work.

About eight o'clock that morning, my office telephone rang. I picked up the receiver.

On the other end, a tiny voice spoke with difficulty. "I love you Daddy," Lori said and disconnected.

I slowly returned the telephone to its cradle.

The picture album had spoken for us.

Our message had been delivered and acknowledged.

THE PHOTOGRAPH BESIDE Lori was of Jason. It was taken in New York City. As it turned out, that trip became the turning point in my life. The story actually began eleven years before. Our sixteen-month-old son had a bad cold and with each of his small rasping breaths, I found mine quickening. Fear gripped my throat. Jason coughed; spittle ran from the side of his mouth in competition with what flowed from his nose. "I'm worried," I said. I saw the scared look on Marilyn's face. Jason was the son we were granted after more than ten years of trying. We had lost one. We wanted this one to survive. "Maybe you should call the doctor?" I said.

Marilyn dialed the doctor's emergency number, only to be told he was away for the weekend. A substitute was taking his calls. The new doctor prescribed an aspirin and suggested Jason would be better in the morning. But Jason's breathing became more laboured, his cough grew worse. Finally I had had enough and told Marilyn we were taking him to Sick Children's Hospital. After a few blocks, I suddenly changed directions, speeding away from our intended destination.

"Where are you going?" Marilyn asked, her voice bordering on panic.

"Branson Hospital. It's closer. I don't like the sound of his breathing."

At the hospital, we hurried to the emergency admittance window where Marilyn blurted out, "My baby can't breathe."

A nurse took Jason away, leaving us to answer the receptionist's questions. A little while later, she returned. "He's settled down. His breathing is irregular. It might be prudent to leave him here overnight, just in case, but I don't think there's anything to worry about." She saw our worried faces. "Would you like to see him?"

We nodded. Marilyn and I held hands as the nurse led us down a long, empty corridor to a large nursery. In a whispered voice, she said, "See. All is well. But I recommend you sign an emergency waiver."

"Why?" I asked.

"Only as a precaution. I'm sure it won't be needed. He'll be all right in the morning, you'll see." Her tone was reassuring. We reluctantly signed the waiver and returned home.

The next morning, before leaving for work, I called the hospital and inquired about Jason. An unemotional voice assured me that everything was fine. I left for my office. Shortly afterwards, Marilyn received a telephone call. The voice said Marilyn should return to the hospital immediately; something had happened to her son. A quick call to me to let me know and we both raced to our cars.

We ran to the room where we had left Jason. A small light illuminated a silhouette of a young woman sitting beside the crib next to the one that had held our son. I asked, "Do you know where the baby who was in the next crib is now?" I asked.

"Are you his parents?" she asked.

I nodded.

"Oh, my God! You don't know?"

"Know what?"

She shook her head, a look of sadness on her face. Her voice became soft and sympathetic. "I came here a couple of hours ago with my daughter. She had a fever and I stayed with her."

"Do you know what happened to my son?"

"About an hour ago, a nurse sat by the crib next to me. I asked if there was a problem. She said she was just keeping an eye on the baby. She'd been with him off and on all night. He was very restless and his nose was running. She would lean over and wipe him. Suddenly, he started gagging and the nurse ran from the room. Everything happened so quickly. One minute she was beside me, the next she was racing through the door. I heard her voice over the loudspeaker repeating the words 'Code Blue' over and over. I ran to the corridor to see what was happening. From every door, stairwell and elevator, doctors and nurses raced into this room, placed the baby onto a gurney and ran down the hall." The look in her eyes spoke volumes and her voice trembled when she concluded, "I haven't seen the baby since, or the nurse."

There was silence as the three of us stared at one another, neither Marilyn nor I knowing what to say, the woman at a loss as to what more she could add. As we turned to leave, a doctor arrived and apologized for being late. Another emergency.

We turned to him, our faces ashen.

He smiled. "Your son's all right," he said.

Marilyn broke down and cried and I valiantly fought back my own tears.

"The congestion in your son's lungs affected his breathing. There was a great deal of mucous in his bronchial tubes. He choked, couldn't get enough oxygen into his lungs and was suffocating. A nurse had volunteered to sit beside his crib. When he started gagging, she called for assistance. It was a good thing you signed the emergency waiver because I had to perform a tracheotomy to get him to breathe again."

I groaned.

"With rest, he should be as good as ever," he quickly added.

As if a lock had sprung open, my body lost its strength and I found myself unable to stop the tears from falling.

Later that week, we took Jason home and over the next year, I discovered that that night was to haunt me for ten more years.

Before going to the hospital, Jason spoke short sentences and showed a good aptitude for understanding and expressing his needs. It was not unusual to see him waddling about the house, talking to himself and pointing at objects as if he were conducting a tour. After the tracheotomy, Marilyn and I noticed he showed little initiative for talking, pointing instead to items that he wanted and grunting.

The doctor assured us that this was temporary. But the weeks turned into months and then a year. Jason never said another word. He became very proficient in grunting and waving his hands, and Marilyn and his two sisters accommodated his gestures by recognizing what the grunts meant and gave in to him without hesitation.

I objected.

"Make him say a few words and he'll realize there's no pain when he talks," I said. They still thought he'd snap out of it, but more months passed and Jason's life was an adventure of learning, seeing, smelling and grunting – but never talking.

My objections peaked one evening while we were having dinner. Jason grunted and pointed to the water pitcher on the table. I knew what he wanted but, without thinking, I asked, "What do you want, Jason?"

Jason grunted again and waved his hand in the direction of the water pitcher.

I made no attempt to accommodate his request. My daughters looked at me, confused at my not giving him what he obviously wanted. I shook my head to let them know that they were not to interfere and showed Jason a stern face.

On the verge of tears, Lori said, "Don't be mean, Dad. You know he wants a glass of water. Let him have it."

Jason grunted louder, his forefinger pointing towards the pitcher.

I ignored Lori's plea. "I'm sorry, Jason," I said "What is it you want?"

Lisa reached for the pitcher.

I grabbed her wrist, making her put it down. "What did you say you wanted, Jason?" I asked again, trying to keep myself calm.

"Stop that, Dad!" Lisa said, "You're going to hurt him."

Marilyn turned to me. "Not now. We'll do this another time. You're upsetting Jason and the girls."

By now, Jason had become agitated. He grunted louder, stretching his arms to reach the water pitcher.

The girls gathered around me pleading. "Daddy, stop! Stop! He's going to hurt himself."

It was hard to ignore their pleas. I faced Marilyn, hoping she understood that what I was doing was necessary, but I saw a worried look on her face. I realized that if I continued, I could be doing more harm than good. My son's grunts had become louder and the girls pleas more insistent. I pushed them away and faced Jason. "Do you want the water, Jason?" My heart raced and I could feel perspiration running under my shirt.

Jason grunted and animatedly waved both his arms.

The girls continued to pull at me. I ordered everyone to leave the kitchen. I pushed them out the door and returned to my seat and faced my angry son. "I'm sorry, Jason. I don't understand what it is you want. Do you want the water?" My voice sounded calm, but a hurricane of emotions beat against my chest. From behind the kitchen door I heard my family pleading. There's nothing wrong with my son, I repeated to myself. There's nothing wrong with him. He can talk. Please, I prayed, say something.

Jason gave me a stern look, his arms clawing the air in the direction of the water pitcher.

The exercise was exhausting me. I didn't think I could hold out much longer.

Jason stared hard at me. Finally, he threw his hands in front of him, pointed to the water pitcher and said, "wha-der". The anger in his tone was obvious. He glared at me. "Wha-der, wha-der," he said, his hand waving all over the table.

"Oh," I said calmly. "You want the water? Why didn't you say so before?" I reached for the water pitcher and poured the clear liquid into Jason's little plastic glass. Jason immediately raised it to his lips and drank.

I rose from my chair and opened the kitchen door to let everyone in. They rushed past me to Jason.

"Wha-der," Jason said, "wha-der."

I could hear them cheering as I left the kitchen. I entered my bedroom, closing the door behind me. The confrontation had drained me. My body shook. I sat on my bed and wept like a child.

When I returned to the kitchen, Lisa was pointing and saying the names of various items on the table. Jason would repeat a word out loud. Everyone cheered and Jason clapped his hands, broadly grinning at the attention he was receiving. I gazed at him, wondering if I had done the right thing? Who had won this battle? I was to learn that I had lost.

The years passed. Jason kept himself aloof from me. He never hugged me back whenever I took him into my arms, he walked beside me, but not near me and he avoided holding my hand. There was dialogue, but not intimacy. At first, I thought it was his way. Even as a little boy he showed a tendency to be a loner. He was not one to ask for anything. He either did it or he avoided it. Was I something he could do without? Had I, in my need to make my son talk, alienated him?

During the course of my business, I often went to the United States, spending about six days buying art. Before one of my trips Marilyn suggested, "Why don't you take Jason with you? The two of you would be alone, without any family distractions, and maybe something would come out of it."

Jason was now eleven. Being alone with my son or going somewhere with him had proven a rare and infrequent treat. I proposed the trip to him and made it appear like a big thing, with side trips to Coney Island and Atlantic City. With some persuasion from his mother and sisters, he reluctantly agreed.

We went sightseeing, but Jason displayed no sign of whether he was enjoying the trip or not. In New York City, we walked along Broadway, Avenue of the Americas and Forty-Second Street. The sidewalks bustled with hawkers shouting to come into the various strip houses, their hands waving gaudy brochures; derelicts lay against buildings clutching paper bags, mounds of garbage littered the sidewalk. Multitudes of rushing people pushed and squeezed their way in both directions, oblivious to the sights and smells being inhaled by a frightened, eleven-year-old boy. Jason walked beside me, with just enough room between us, as if another person had been there. His eyes were wide, but not with wonder as I first thought, but with fear. The open space between us gradually narrowed. Several young girls in very low-cut tops and short skirts blocked Jason's path. One remarked on how cute he looked. "Good enough to eat," she said as she swept her tongue slowly around her lips. The girls laughed and went on their way. Then I recognized the fear in Jason's face.

We continued walking. I felt a soft touch against my hand as Jason's fingers locked into mine. I felt my heart racing. "Do you want to go away from here?" I asked.

He nodded.

I quickly led him away from the noise and clamber of activity and, all the while, his hand remained locked in mine even after we left Forty-Second Street. His small hand was lost in mine and yet it was I who felt lost in his. The touch of his hand told me I was to be trusted. It told me my son wanted my protection. It told me Jason had faith that I would keep him safe.

Soon, Jason would return my love and take away my pain.

And he did.

I LOOKED TO the telephone. Had I missed its ring? I listened intently, hoping it would break the silence in the room. I moved over to a bookcase and came to a photograph of Lisa. Lisa, the rebel. If ever there was a child that challenged life, it was she.

At fourteen, Lisa was filled with anger directed at Marilyn and me. She was the model of how parents make mistakes when raising their first born. It appeared that Lisa interpreted the many hours Marilyn and I spent doing community volunteer work as a rejection of her. To her it meant we did not love her. There were times she would withdraw into herself, leaving the impression that she would do herself harm just to spite us, to make us suffer for denying her the love she wanted. When I realized the problem, nothing I could do or say took away her anger and any attempt we made to find a middle ground was futile – until I left for Los Angeles to attend a five-day learning conference.

At the airport, Marilyn straightened my tie and pushed a lock of hair away from my forehead. The airport was crowded and boarding had been announced. "Be careful," she said, a worried look on her face.

"Stop fussing. I'll be all right." But the grin on my face said otherwise. I hated flying. "How long do I have to be married before you stop sending me away like I'm just a kid?"

"But you are a kid. My big kid." She smiled.

I frowned. "The kid at home may give you some trouble. Can you handle it?"

Marilyn's smile disappeared. "No. Her behaviour tears me apart. We love her. Why can't she see that?"

"I don't know, dear. Just be careful what you say. Lisa's smart but she's confused. Tread softly while I'm gone. Okay?"

Marilyn smiled again. "Kiss?"

"No passion," I whispered, "just a kiss." My laughter was cut off by her lips on mine.

When I arrived at the hotel, there was a message waiting for me. I called immediately, thinking something terrible had happened. "Marilyn, what's the matter?" I asked.

"I did something I wasn't supposed to do and I discovered something I'm not supposed to know."

"What?"

"Lisa is smoking!"

"How do you know?"

"I was putting away her laundry and I found an open pack of cigarettes in her dresser drawer." Her voice sounded shaky.

I drew a deep breath, striving for calm. "You're not supposed to go into her room, you know that. She's very protective of her turf. And now that you know, how are you going to confront her with it, since you found out by doing something you were not supposed to do?"

"I don't know. It's not the smoking I'm concerned about, it's that I don't think she realizes what her decision could do to her future. And what if she's doing it just to, I don't know, get back at us or something?"

I could tell that Marilyn was crying. "Say nothing, honey. When I come back in a week, I'll think of what to do."

"What can you do? She wouldn't listen to us before, so why would she listen now?"

"I don't know. Let me think about it. Meanwhile, say nothing. Agreed?"

Marilyn agreed.

The problem was mine to resolve, but I didn't know how. There was a rivalry between Lisa and Marilyn. If Marilyn said "up," Lisa said, "down." If Marilyn said, "in," Lisa said "out." No matter the issue, they seemed to lock horns on it. With me being away more often than not, I had become the father figure who avoided a confrontation. My major concern was that cigarettes today might mean harmful drugs tomorrow. She was young and impressionable. This was one confrontation I knew I could not walk away from.

The week ended but I still didn't have an answer. At dinner the evening I returned home, I made no mention to Lisa of what her mother had found in her dresser. After she finished eating, she left the table and went to her room. Marilyn and I watched her leave. I shook my head in resignation, then rose from the table to confront Lisa about the cigarettes.

I knocked on her door and asked if I could come in. My visits to her room were infrequent and usually were efforts to resolve some difference. I had a tendency to speak very formally, somewhat unemotionally, and this, combined with my preoccupation with my own needs, had created a barrier between us – a barrier that widened whenever I asked Lisa questions about school or her friends. Unfortunately, Lisa was very astute and detected a lack of sincerity in my queries.

Once, when I asked how she was doing in school, she replied, "Why?"

"I'm interested," I had said.

"Why?" she persisted. "Are you interested for me or for yourself?"

"What do you mean, for myself?"

Lisa stared at me, a challenge in her eyes. "I'm not sure you really care how I'm doing. I think you're only interested to find out if my marks are high enough not to embarrass you."

I fumbled for an answer. "I only asked the question for the question's sake. I had no ulterior motive."

"Then why do you ask only when I'm having exams and not any other times during the year? Seems you're only interested when my marks are at stake." The conversation ended, but her meaning was not lost on me.

Her answers about her social life were equally evasive. I'd ask her, "Where are you going tonight?"

"Out."

"Where?"

"Someplace."

"With whom?"

"A friend."

"When will you be back?"

"Later."

Communication, to say the least, was short, abrupt and unsatisfactory. Facing me now was the problem of how to open the door and say what I wanted to say before it was slammed in my face. Although my daughter defended her wall, I needed to find a crack in it. At her "Come in," I entered to find her sitting on her bed reading a school book.

"May I sit?" I asked. "I think we should talk."

Without lifting her eyes from her book, Lisa nodded.

The first dilemma was what to sit on. Being six-foot-three and weighing over 275 pounds could present a problem in Lisa's room. The only extra chair was built for a child, and to sit on it was a bit of a balancing act. I feared I'd look like a clown and it is difficult to be taken serious when you look like a clown. Nevertheless, I sat on it and focused on Lisa. "I don't know how to say this except straight out."

"What?"

"I understand you've taken up smoking."

I watched as Lisa's eyes narrow and her lips tighten. It was like watching a volcano steam before the lava gushed out. "I want to apologize for your mother. She opened your dresser drawer to put your laundered clothes in and saw the cigarettes. She told me about her discovery and I would like to discuss your decision to smoke."

Lisa's face took on a reddish hue.

"I wonder if you are really aware of the full implications of your decision," I blurted out. "If you want to smoke, I won't stop you. My only concern is that you realize what smoking will mean to your future; the long-term factors involved."

Lisa's eyes opened wide in surprise. "You mean you'll let me smoke?"

"Yes, if that's what you want."

"I really don't need your permission anyway," she said. "I'm fourteen. I'm old enough to make my own decisions. I'm not a child."

I looked at my young daughter who was desperately trying to act like an adult and knew exactly how she felt. I remembered, in that instant, my mother catching me when I was thirteen with a pack of cigarettes and how she had handled it. I took the same position my mother had taken with me. "I don't approve, but I won't stop you. But I would like to make sure you're aware of what you're doing and why I don't approve. Will you listen to me?"

She nodded.

Now that I had her attention, I talked about the effects of smoking, especially as it pertained to sports. Lisa had a passion for running and was active in track and field. There was an excitement on her face when she competed, an exhilaration I could relate to, having experienced it myself. Gravity ceased to exist. It was freedom from weight. I, too, had loved to run when I was in school. Because I was a borderline asthmatic, though, I told her how I had struggled to excel because my lungs could not hold the oxygen I needed. I told Lisa that she was swifter than I ever was; she had a grace and symmetry that rarely comes without formal training. Smoking would take that away. She listened in silence.

"Why did you start smoking?" I asked.

Lisa looked down at the carpet.

"Peer pressure?"

She remained silent.

"It is sometimes harder to be yourself than it is to imitate others." No response.

"There is more to being an adult than just being older, Lisa. Often it takes strength of character, so your peers will accept you for who you are and not for who you aren't."

Lisa jumped to her feet and ran from the room into the bathroom, closing the door behind her. She was crying. I waited, hoping she would return. But, as the minutes passed, I was about to accept that our conversation was over when I heard the bathroom door open. She came back into the bedroom, her face washed and her voice soft. "I'll think about what you said."

I stood up, relieved the chair had not collapsed under me. I wanted to take her in my arms and tell her growing up can be a wonderful experience as long as you watch out for the pitfalls. I would have liked to kiss away the pain she was going through, but I didn't have the courage. Instead, I said, "This may be the first day of your adult life – think about the direction you want to go. It's sometimes too hard to erase a mistake," and I left her room, closing the door behind me.

Lisa never smoked again. Her passion for running increased, first with biathlons and then triathlons. When she grew up, she became an adventurer. She lived in the bush in Africa, one time counting gorillas, another counting elephants and rhinos. She has also climbed Mount Kilimanjaro in Tanzania and spent six weeks living in the Greater Kitlope rain forest of British Columbia with the Haisla Nation.

She challenged a former employer, a marathon runner, to a thirteen-kilometre race. She wagered that if she beat him, he would double her pledges to the Koffler Breast Cancer Foundation. She beat him and together they donated thousands of dollars to the fund. The following year, she was part of a running team that raised more than double for the same fund.

When she was in university, I asked her how she was doing during the school year, not only at exam time. When we speak, I've learned to pay attention to what she says, rather than just hear her words. I discovered a very important fact from that experience. Just as I sought respect and recognition from my peers, she sought the same from her parents. And most importantly, the wall between us crumbled.

Now that she is older, I definitely don't ask where she's going and how late she'll be out. Just as we get used to her being back in the city, she's gone again, backpacking through Peru, Thailand, Malaysia, Indonesia, India, Nepal, the Amazon Jungles and God knows where.

If I had remained silent . . .?

I TURNED MY back abruptly from the bookcase. My eyes were moist. Memories, I thought. Will that be all I have left? I glared at the telephone again, willing it to ring with news of Marilyn. But it mocked me with its silence. I didn't want to lose her. We were still young. I wanted to call the hospital again. I'd already done it twice, but the receptionist had nothing to tell me. I could detect an annoyance in her tone when I called the last time. I glanced again at the telephone, then turned back to the photographs.

All by itself on a shelf was the most precious of all photographs. It showed Marilyn and me in front of our 1960 blue Ford; the one she had crashed before we were married. It had been a silly accident. It had happened on a Sunday morning. There were eight empty lanes on the Lakeshore and she had driven into a parked car while making a left turn. The policeman who came to investigate couldn't stop laughing at what she had done.

"I'll never drive again," Marilyn wailed.

I spoke to the photograph. "You used to stutter when this was taken. Every time you had a problem, out came the stuttering."

I groaned and whispered Marilyn's name, hoping to hear her answering. All I heard was my own heart beating too fast. I returned to the couch, dropped onto it and closed my eyes. A scene came to me of Marilyn and Lisa in the kitchen. I saw myself walk in; I was young, cocky and overconfident.

"T-t-teach me how to sell," Marilyn stuttered.

I laughed. "That's ridiculous. You can't talk and, besides, you can't drive a car. You haven't driven since that crazy accident."

Every day she persisted with her plea. "I-I-I want to learn how to sell. T-teach me."

Finally I told her, "If you learn how to drive, I'll teach you to sell."

Marilyn stopped asking. I thought the matter was behind me. Three months later, at the dinner table, Marilyn placed a covered silver tray before me. I looked at the tray and then at Marilyn. She smiled at me. Lisa giggled.

"What's inside?" I asked.

Marilyn took her seat. "Open the lid and f-find out."

"It can't be food, dinner's still on the stove."

"Open the l-l-lid." She sounded like a machine gun.

I gave a nervous laugh. "It's not my birthday."

Lisa was jumping up and down on her seat, enjoying the suspense.

"Okay." I removed the lid. Lying on the tray was a sheet of paper, folded in half.

"What's this?"

"R-read it," Marilyn said.

I opened the sheet. It was a temporary driver's license.

Marilyn stammered, "N-n-now that I have my driver's license, t-t-teach me how to sell."

The clock chimed and the scene faded. "Oh, God!" I moaned. I rose to my feet, placed my hands over my ears and stared at the telephone. "Ring!" I hollered. "Make a noise."

I heard footsteps running down the hall and Lisa entered my bedroom. "Are you all right, Dad?"

"I'm fine. I'm sorry. Did I wake you?"

"No, I couldn't sleep. I guess you haven't heard anything?"

"Nothing, yet. I just shouted at the phone." Lisa looked at me with tears in her eyes. I extended my arms to her and she ran into them, crying against my shoulder.

"I keep thinking about her," she sobbed.

"So do I. I was recalling the time she got her driver's license. You were eight then. Do you remember?"

Lisa sniffed. She laughed softly.

"What's so funny?"

"The look on your face when she cornered you with your promise. I can see you staring at the license with your mouth open. You looked so funny."

"Your mother is not someone to take for granted."

"I know. Do you remember the first time she made a sales call by herself?"

I smiled. It broadened as I recalled that evening. "She went to sell Thank You cards to a couple whose Bar Mitzvah order we had already done. She had been going with me for over a month on my sales calls, watching me make my presentation. She spoke little because she was nervous and when she was nervous, you know what happened."

Lisa laughed. "T-t-t-t-t."

We laughed together.

"Everything was against her. She was nervous, it was dark and she had to drive by herself. I wished her good luck as she left the house. I thought she would cave in and not go, but she left. One hour passed, two, then three. She was gone too long. The clock approached midnight and there was still no word from your mother. I was tempted to call the client and ask if your mother was still there, but I was afraid that, if I did, it would destroy her confidence. Losing the sale was not important. Failure might undo the changes your mother was undergoing."

"You mean the stuttering."

"Yes. She talked more and that was good. The more she talked, the more confident she grew. Well, shortly after midnight, I heard the key in the lock and was prepared for tears and remorse. I was surprised when she bounced into the room beaming from ear to ear. Did you make the sale?" I said.

"Oh, yes. It took about half an hour, but they were so nice I stayed for coffee and we started to talk about who we knew."

I rolled my eyes and laughed. "Your mother taught me a lesson that night that has stayed with me ever since. Nothing is impossible if you want it bad enough."

Lisa nodded her head. "She doesn't stutter anymore."

"No, she doesn't."

Lisa sighed. "I'm tired. I'm going to lie down."

"I'll call you." I took my daughter in my arms and hugged her.

The telephone rang.

I looked at Lisa. Her face had tightened. Fear was in her eyes.

The telephone rang.

I placed my hand over the receiver and closed my eyes.

The telephone rang.

I picked it up.

"Hello," I whispered. My face slackened as I listened to the voice of the doctor. I nodded a few times and looked over at Lisa's frightened face. My lips trembled. A tear made its way down my cheek. "Thank you," I said. I looked at the receiver in my hand before placing it back in its cradle. I turned to Lisa and a tired smile appeared. "She's going to be okay," I said. "All she needs now is our love."

The Coat That Wouldn't Die

LILLIAN SAX, A volunteer at a Toronto seniors' centre, first noticed Sarah Perlstein the week she came in wearing an old, torn cloth coat. The left pocket seam was torn, the sleeves worn, and two ragged strips of the lining hung below the hem. The garment had obviously seen better days and, by its style, couldn't have been very expensive when it was new. No amount of cajoling from people who knew her could persuade her either to fix it or replace it.

Sarah, a widow, was no more than five feet tall and had a slight hunch to her back and a shuffling walk. No one knew exactly how old she was, but Lillian guessed at about seventy-five. After some inquiries, Lillian learned she was originally from Poland and had been in a concentration camp during those terrible years of the war, but she never talked about her experiences. In fact, Sarah wasn't much of a talker.

As the weeks passed and the weather became colder, her concern for Sarah Perlstein and her torn coat grew. Finally Lillian approached the old woman.

"Hello, Mrs. Perlstein," she said when Sarah came into the cafeteria. "My name is Lillian Sax. I'm a volunteer."

Sarah smiled. "I've seen you several times."

"I was wondering if I could help you. Maybe I could have your coat repaired for you."

Self-consciously Sarah pressed the torn pocket flap against the fabric so that it didn't look for the moment as if it was torn, smiled and said, "It'll be all right. It's fine."

"Are you sure?"

"Yes, thank you."

"I understand you're a Holocaust survivor from Poland?" Lillian said.

Sarah stopped smiling. "Yes."

"Do you find it difficult to talk about what happened?"

Sarah's lips trembled. "Sometimes," she said.

"How old were you when the war started?"

Sarah stared at the ceiling before replying. "Fourteen."

"Your coat, did you bring it to Canada?"

Sarah nodded.

"There must be a story behind why you've kept it so long. Would you like to tell me about it?"

There was a pause before she answered, "I'm sorry. I'd rather not."

"Maybe another time?"

"Maybe."

A FEW WEEKS later, Lillian knocked on Sarah's apartment door. "Would you like some company?"

"Why thank you," Sarah said as she opened the door. "That would be nice. This is unexpected. Are you just coming from the centre?" she asked.

"Yes, I haven't seen you there this week and was concerned."

"Oh, I'm fine. Sometimes I just like to be alone."

"I understand your husband died a few years ago. Do you have children?"

"No. It wasn't possible."

The old woman had to stretch to reach the coat bar in the closet and Lillian helped, placing her coat on a hanger. Lillian pointed to the coat with the torn pocket hanging beside hers and shook her head.

"Do you know there was a time when I could have fixed it good as new myself?" Sarah said.

"You were a seamstress?"

"Yes. It was what saved my life. It was another time."

"I'm sure you realize it might be more practical to buy a new one."

Sarah became solemn. "I know," she said. "I've had it since 1954. It was the first new coat I owned since before the war."

"Why won't you fix it?"

Sarah suddenly gripped her left hand, which shook uncontrollably. She gave a low moan.

Lillian was frightened. "Are you all right, Sarah?"

"Yes, yes. It will go away. Sometimes my hand takes on a life of its own. Anyway, at my age, I don't need a new coat. If I buy a new coat, it will outlive me." She laughed, but there was no joy in the sound.

"No, Sarah, it will keep you warm and extend your life."

"To tell you the truth, I've lived long enough and seen too much. I have much to forget."

"But Sarah, talking helps. I'm a good listener. Won't you talk to me? I would like to know you better."

"Why would you want to know me?"

Lillian smiled. "Why wouldn't I?"

Sarah grinned. "My story is no different from others. I am from Lodz. When the bombs came, my younger brother was already at work. He never returned. Our house was near the factories and was destroyed. Somehow I lived. My parents did not."

"You never heard from your brother again?"

"Nothing. I can't even remember what he looks like. Too many years and too many bad memories have removed his face from my eyes. But I remember the last time I saw him. As he left for work, he was excited. The owner promised to show him how to use a sewing machine that day. He was only thirteen. I boiled him an egg and gave him a slice of black bread with homemade jam I made. I remember asking him what he thought of the jam." Sarah paused and closed her eyes for a moment. "He said it was as sweet as his favourite sister. I laughed because I was his only sister. He put on his cap and went out the door – forever."

"What happened to you?" Lillian asked.

"A ghetto was formed. I was put to work making uniforms. When they liquidated the ghetto, I was sent to a labour camp to make German winter coats, and later to Buchenwald. I survived. I saw too much. My left hand didn't start to shake until after the war. It was my left hand that guided the cloth through the machine. Maybe I'm being punished for surviving." Sarah had tears in her eyes and her hand shook.

Lillian reached out and gently took her hand, then held it until it stopped shaking. "I don't think you're being punished. It's your body reminding you of what it had to endure."

Sarah gave a tired smile. "Thank you for caring."

"Let me care some more. Let me buy you a new coat."

"Buy me a coat? Does it mean that much to you?"

"Yes. A new coat from a new friend. Let me do this for you."

Sarah laughed. "All right. I'll get a new coat. But I'll pay for it. I have the money. It was never the money."

"I know," Lillian said.

A FEW DAYS later, Lillian drove to a street off Spadina Avenue and parked. Then she and Sarah entered a building and climbed the narrow steps to the second floor where there were racks and racks of men's suits and jackets and all types of cloth coats. The owner appeared and was told of their need.

"Come with me," he said, and took them to a rack.

Sarah was very cooperative and smiled often when she tried on the different coats. Finally they came to a decision and she admired herself in the full-length mirror. The owner nodded his approval at their selection and left to get the tailor. He returned with an elderly man who had a thin tape measure hung around his neck and lapels filled with pins. The tailor eyed the coat hanging on Sarah's stooped body. His head bobbed a few times. He stuck a pin into the coat, pulled on the shoulders, pinched the back where it hung loosely, tightened his grip on the cloth and stuck in another pin. A pin here, a pin there, his hands constantly gliding gently over Sarah's back and slight frame.

The smile had left the old woman's face. She seemed uncomfortable. Her eyes moved in the direction of the tailor's hands as they passed over her shoulders. Lillian and the owner were in conversation and didn't appear to be aware of Sarah's discomfort. Sarah's hand began to shake uncontrollably. She gave a moan and gripped her arm. The tailor stopped what he was doing and stepped back. Lillian and the owner stopped talking and stared at her.

"Lillian, I would like to leave," Sarah pleaded.

"He's not finished."

"I'm sorry," she answered. "I can't stay." She removed the new coat, retrieved her own and before it was on her, was hurrying down the steps to the street.

Lillian apologized to the owner and hurried after her. On the street, she saw Sarah standing by the curb, tears in her eyes. "Are you all right, Sarah?"

"I'm sorry," she said. "That was foolish of me."

"Are you all right?"

"Yes. Yes. I'm sorry. We'll come back another time."

"What was the matter?"

"It was his hands. I had the strangest feeling when the tailor's hands touched me. I don't know how to explain it, but as his hands moved along my back and shoulders, I had this feeling that it was my brother's hands on me. My brother was learning to be a tailor. He would practise on me as if I had a coat, and his hands were gentle, just like that man's."

"Are you all right now?" Lillian asked.

"Yes."

They walked to the car and Lillian opened the passenger door. Sarah didn't get in. "I've kept this coat all these years because it reminded me of my brother. I would remember how he fussed at me as if I had on a coat and he was altering it. The coat became my only link to a good memory from my past." She turned to look at the building.

"I'm sorry, Sarah. I didn't mean to upset you."

Sarah continued to stare at the building. "I would like to go back," she said. "I want to ask his name."

"Maybe you should wait and sleep on it."

Sarah placed her hand gently on Lillian's arm and shook her head. Without waiting for an answer, Sarah returned to the building.

Sarah was out of breath when she reached the floor. Lillian stood behind her, a look of concern on her face. The owner and the tailor had been talking as Sarah approached. The owner stepped away from the tailor. Sarah stood before the tailor and stared at him for long moments not saying a word.

He looked back at her, smiling.

"What do you think of the jam I made?" Sarah hesitantly asked.

The tailor's brow knitted in a frown and a momentary look of confusion appeared on his face. He stared hard at Sarah Perlstein for what seemed an eternity, then the lines on his face softened and in a low whisper, he answered, "It's as sweet as my favourite sister."

Forbidden

(Excerpt from: An Eye For An Eye)

Dateline: August 31, 1939

JANUSZ STRADDLED THE footrest as he listened to the crackling of the radio. He removed his uniform jacket, opened his collar and loosened his tie to make himself comfortable. The news was not good. It hadn't been for days. German tanks were massing near the Polish borders.

He cursed Hitler. It was all too apparent that the German Fuhrer never had any intention of giving so much as a millimetre in his so-called negotiations with the Polish government. He was prepared to invade Poland. Janusz knew the Polish government expected England and France to produce a last-minute miracle, but too much depended on hope and not enough on self-initiative.

Since promising to meet Rachel, he had received new orders to be at the local headquarters, the Museum in Sienkiewicza Park, in Lodz, which had been commandeered, before one in the morning. If that wasn't a sign of imminent disaster, nothing was. He glanced furtively at the front door. Rachel had sounded desperate when he'd talked to her on the telephone that afternoon. She alluded that her father suspected she was seeing him. He sensed she would be the bearer of more bad news.

He heard a soft tap on the door and switched off the radio, then looked around the room to make sure everything was neat and tidy. He shot a quick glance towards the bedroom door to make sure it was closed before opening the front door, his expression composed to hide his anxiety.

She hesitantly entered. Janusz had anticipated a kiss, but Rachel breezed passed him.

"It's a beautiful night," she said, "but there's hardly anyone out." Her light tone belied the strained look on her face. "Nice apartment," she added as she moved around the room examining the pictures on the walls and the furniture.

Janusz nodded, then locked the door. He crossed to the couch and sat on the arm as he watched her, waiting to hear words he didn't want to hear. "It's not good at home, is it?" he finally asked.

Rachel stopped and looked at him, then shook her head. She lowered herself into a tub chair, smoothed her full, ankle-length skirt, then placed her hands on her lap, her fingers fidgeting as she avoided looking at Janusz.

"Do you want to talk about it?"

Rachel continued to fidget and avoid eye contact.

Janusz got to his feet.

"No, stay there, please!" Rachel said, motioning with her hands for him to sit.

Confused, Janusz lowered himself back onto the arm. "You want to tell me you can't see me any more because of your father?" he said.

Tears appeared in Rachel's eyes. "Janusz, there are so many obstacles."

"I understand. I believe we can overcome the obstacles." He was having difficulty keeping his voice steady.

"We come from different faiths, Janusz. You don't realize how big the obstacles are," she whispered.

"But I do. They are the same for me as they are for you. When I returned to Warsaw, I decided to tell my father about you."

Rachel's head snapped up and for the first time their eyes met. "Oh, Janusz!"

Janusz exhaled a long breath. "My father is a generous and fair person. We've always had a good relationship. And yet, when I left his office last week, I knew the bond we'd had was broken . . ." His voice trailed off. There was a tortured look on his face as he grasped for words. "You see, he expected his only son to marry a Catholic as your father expected you to marry someone Jewish. He has unshakeable faith in the church and what it represents. Your father, from what you've told me, is just as committed to his faith. The last thing I wanted to do was hurt him or my family, but Rachel . . . Rachel, if I was to have any kind of a future with you, they had to know of you." The words rushed from his lips, his voice rising.

Rachel removed a handkerchief from her purse and dabbed her eyes. "Janusz, we are causing so much pain."

"I know, but it can't be avoided. When I first walked into his office, he hugged me. We hadn't seen each other for more than a month. We celebrated with a glass of brandy which my father kept for special occasions. He couldn't stop smiling as he gazed at me in my uniform and I saw the pride in his eyes. If my feelings for you were not so strong, I think I would have backed down and left without saying a word . . . but I finally told him. I cannot describe the change that came

over him as I told him of my love for you. He insisted I talk to Father
Leszkiewicz, our parish priest, before I made any final decisions."

"Did you?"

"I've known Father Leszkiewicz all my life, watched his kindness
as he administered more than faith to his parishioners. I've gone to
him when I couldn't find answers to problems that disturbed me.
Always he was someone I could talk to. Whatever advice he gave me,
whether I accepted it or not, I knew he was sincere. I came to his
office because my father had asked me to, but I did not intend to
relent. When I lived in Germany, I saw things there that I never
realized before. I never knew that I, too, lived in a ghetto, a ghetto of
Catholics. A ghetto of people who thought alike, prayed alike, even
walked alike. We were copies of one another. In Germany, there was a
mixture of nationalities, of religious preferences and, in some cases, of
colour. University students from around the globe came to study and
brought the world closer together. I saw how different this was from
my world and wondered why I never saw it before.

"I sat in Father Leszkiewicz's office. It was an ugly room in the
church rectory with dark wood panelling on the walls, pictures of the
Catholic hierarchy hanging in the room and behind the Father's huge
oak desk a large cross with the saviour, Jesus Christ, staring down at
the chair in which he had sat. The room was not designed for comfort,
but for intimidation. When I told Father Leszkiewicz why I was there,
I saw the hurt in his eyes and heard the pain in his voice as he tried to
persuade me from my course. I had challenged him.

"The memory of that confrontation is most vivid in my mind.
'Does the Church not understand love?' I asked.

"Father Leszkiewicz spoke with reserved calm. 'Yes, but not
romantic love. It can't be trusted, and there is no way you can be
assured it will last. Once you enter into this unholy alliance, you break
the commitment you made at baptism, which you consciously re-
affirmed in the sacrament of confirmation. You have been sealed and
therefore you belong to Christ and you have a commitment to spread
the Faith and build up the Church. Are you building up the Church
when you marry someone who is not a Catholic? Is commitment
something that is on today, off tomorrow and on again later because
your feelings change? You made the commitment. It is you who wants

to break that trust. It is not me that you must ask for understanding, it is Him.'"

Janusz had refused to look above the priest's head. "You're asking me to deny my feelings?"

"No, I'm asking you to realize what you are asking. Life does not end because of a tragedy. Your life will not be over because you are confronted with an unhappy choice. Another will enter your life, someone of our faith who will remove that pain you are feeling now."

"The Church is too rigid."

"No. The Church sees us beyond the grave and it must be taken into account in the major decisions of our lives. Faith is a healer. You want to ignore your Faith and its teachings. That is not possible."

"The father of the girl I love thinks as you do, he exclaimed. Both of you seem so sure of yourselves. Are you saying that both of you are right? But why am I wrong?"

"The Jewish faith is fine as far as it goes, but it is incomplete. Yes, they believe in the one true God, the God of Abraham, as do we. But their faith is incomplete without Jesus Christ. They do not know this and that is why they are so adamant about what they do believe. We believe all that they believe and more. You must go forward with Jesus Christ. That is why you cannot do what you desire. You think your heart will break. Not true. It will be your soul that will be damned."

"If I accept your argument, my heart will be damned for the rest of my living life and if I reject my heart, my soul will be damned for eternity. You offer no alternatives."

"Yes, there is an alternative. She can become a Catholic. You can start a Catholic family. You, your wife, your children will all be Catholic."

"I can't ask that of her."

"If she is unwilling to convert, we need an assurance that your children will be baptized and brought up as Catholics. If your children are baptized, their eternal salvation is assured, at least until such time as they attain the use of reason. If they are not baptized and they die before attaining the use of reason, they go to Limbo for all eternity. She has to agree to this and she must sign a statement to that effect. Then we can ask the Bishop's permission. He will grant you a dispensation. It is not a happy solution, but it is an alternative. However, you will be married in the sacristy, not in the Church."

"Why not in the Church?"

"Because you are putting your faith in danger, as well as that of your innocent children. Your eternal salvation is at stake. God does not condemn those outside the Church who know nothing about faith and baptism, but He will not be so understanding of those who, once they have received baptism, either leave the Church or do not live up to their obligations. You must realize the risk you are assuming."

"It is a risk I'll have to take. I cannot impose what you require on someone who has asked nothing of me but my love."

Janusz closed his eyes briefly, the memory of that conversation filling him with misery. "It went badly," he said to Rachel. "I was taught that God was merciful. I begged Father Leszkiewicz for understanding. But he condemned my motives as selfish. I left, knowing that if we married, I would be damned in the eyes of the Church and would create a rift in my family that may never heal."

He looked up and met Rachel's gaze. "My parents were silent when I told them I hadn't changed my mind. I saw the look of surprise on my sister's face. My mother asked if I was prepared to give up everything for you. I told her I was. Then she did something surprising. She came over and gave me a kiss. 'I hope you don't regret what you are doing,' she said. 'I expect you'll live in Lodz.' I said yes."

Rachel stared at him. "And your father?"

"My father . . . well, he wouldn't even look at me. Your father is like my father – a hard person to change. But maybe with time . . ." He sighed. "So you see, I know how you're feeling. I was afraid too. I think with time and, given the chance, my parents will come to love you."

"Oh, Janusz, can you ignore your church?"

"For you? Yes."

"We will be outcasts. Belonging nowhere."

"We will have each other."

Rachel stood. "Janusz. What we're doing will only cause pain to us and to our families."

"Our pain will never go away. Theirs, time could lessen. Without you, I have no life."

Their gaze remained locked. When Rachel spoke again, her voice was very soft. "Janusz, when I came here I had already decided what I wanted to do. Now, especially after what you've said." She dropped her gaze and stared at her hands. "I need you to do something for me."

"Anything."

Rachel smiled and took a deep breath. "Janusz . . . I want you to make love to me tonight? I want you to know that I love you." She closed her eyes as the words left her lips.

Anticipating something quite different, Janusz was stunned. Rachel's eyes remained closed, as if she were afraid to see his reaction to her words.

"Are you sure you understand what you're asking?"

"Of course!" Rachel's eyes opened wide. "We're not children, Janusz." Rachel's voice broke and tears formed in her eyes. "I love you more than I thought was possible, and you love me. You're going to war. People die in wars. Can you guarantee you will return? And what will I have of you if you don't? Words, a touch, an unfulfilled promise?" She shook her head. "I need more. You are my only love. What I'm asking is to be loved by the man I love, the man who loves me." She moved closer and put her arms around him. "Hold me, Janusz. Make love to me. Make me a part of you."

"Listen, my darling." Janusz gently pushed her back and held her at arm's length. "I must leave at midnight. Let's wait until I return. You will see – I will come back. You don't have to prove you love me. I know you do, as I love you."

"You don't understand, Janusz. I ask this not to prove, but to satisfy my love. I don't know if I have the courage to tell my father how I feel, but I have the strength to want your love."

"We'll find a way when I return."

"And . . . and if you don't return –"

"No, Rachel. Don't think like that. I will return. You –"

She put a finger to his lips to silence him. "If you don't return, I want to have at least the memory of our lovemaking . . . I want to remember you if I have to with lasting memories and I know, if we make love, you will give me those memories. This is not for desire, Janusz, this is for me to cherish forever."

Janusz pulled Rachel to him and kissed her hard. He felt her arms around his neck as his lips gently caressed her cheeks, her temples and her neck. Her body trembled, but he made no attempt to go beyond the kiss.

RACHEL PULLED HERSELF away, her smile teasing him with her challenge. "Do you have any idea what it took to ask you?"

"Yes, my love, I think I do, but what you ask . . ."

"Janusz, I want this more than anything else in the world."

"Every nerve in my body cries out to fulfil your wish. If I told you that this has not been in my dreams more times than I can remember would be a lie, but . . ."

"Then make both our dreams come true."

Janusz pressed his lips against Rachel's. Her breathing increased as she savoured the release of the emotions she had always suppressed. She felt his tongue exploring her mouth. His hands slipped under her sweater, pausing on her bare skin. Electricity seemed to discharge from the tips of his fingers as every nerve ending in her body thirsted for contact. The small hairs on the back of her neck rose as he caressed her skin. Slowly, gracefully, he peeled away the forbidden doors that had been locked. Rachel placed her lips against Janusz's ear and whispered, "Shouldn't we turn out the lights?"

"Turn off the lights?" Janusz repeated. He gently pushed her back, "Why?"

"Doesn't everyone turn off the lights when they make love?"

"If I did, how can I see what I'm enjoying?" He brought her towards him, kissing her neck, her throat, her chin as his hands slid up her bare back.

Rachel closed her eyes as she offered her lips to him again. His fingers pushed under her brassiere strap and withdrew, never losing contact with her skin, teasing her with the anticipation of his touch, edging closer to her breasts, then gently stroking the softness of their curves.

She shuddered.

The probing of his fingertips stopped.

She sensed his fingers hovering over his next point of contact. She held her breath.

An eternity seemed to pass before both forefingers gently made contact with her nipples at the same time.

Rachel's breathing exploded.

His hands had taken command as he lifted and massaged with his fingertips, always finishing their movement with her nipples. Drops of perspiration trickled down her spine. All the while, Janusz's tongue was like the touch of silk as it followed the contour of her neck to the upper portion of her cleavage.

She felt his fingers searching for the buttons to release her skirt. She pulled back slightly, not knowing what was expected of her. His groping fingers found and released the button, then pushed her skirt, slip and underwear down her thighs, letting them fall around her ankles, his hands resting on her buttocks. Rachel moaned softly as he explored, kneading the softness of her cheeks. Her legs lost their strength and she leaned against him as his fingers inched towards the triangle of black hair. Her pulse pounded in her ears.

Unexpectedly, Janusz lifted her into his arms. The clothing around her ankles dropped to the floor. Surprised, Rachel opened her eyes. He carried her into the bedroom and gently placed her on the bed, lifted her sweater and open brassiere from her and gazed at her naked body.

A BREEZE SLIPPED through the open window, blowing the curtain away from the sill. The moon shone through, casting a yellow glow on the two naked bodies on the bed. Janusz's leg was draped over Rachel's thigh, his body pressing her to the mattress, her arm over his shoulder, locked in a long passionate kiss as they rolled and turned against each other, their mouths fastened together, their breathing heavy.

Janusz positioned himself between her legs and let his tongue run down her belly, leaving a trail of moisture from her navel to her inner thighs. He dipped his tongue into her, causing her body to arch in slow circular motions and when he penetrated deeper, she pushed her hips against his face.

Small sounds escaped from Rachel's lips.

Janusz mounted her and entered, withdrew and entered again. She emitted a gasp of pain and then the sensations came like none she had ever experienced. Her hands gripped the sides of the mattress as her hips sank into its softness, then heaved into the first spasm of orgasm.

Rachel's body arched upwards. Janusz met her next thrust; his body, no longer under his control, shook and shuddered with each consecutive orgasm. When he at last was drained, he withdrew from within her.

Rachel opened her eyes and smiled, her breathing returning to normal.

Janusz lay on his back, his hand found Rachel's and held it tightly. There was a moment of silence, their breathing the only sound in the room. "Unbelievable," Janusz whispered, contentedly. He moved closer to Rachel and kissed the curve of her breast, tasting the hardness of a nipple and the salt of her perspiration. Rachel pushed him into a sitting position, his back against the bed frame and moved her hand slowly down his body. She stroked the hair on his chest, moved her hand down to his belly, stopping at his pubic hair. "Janusz, what happens tomorrow?"

There was a long pause before he answered. "Like you said, we will live on our memories until the war is over, my sweet. It can't last too long."

Rachel's hand continued to his penis, swallowing the head with the palm of her hand, stroking it vigorously, feeling it harden. She laughed softly.

"What's so funny?"

"I think my memory is fading. Can we do it again?" she said, as she leaned forward and impaled herself between his legs.

THE EVENING HAD remained warm. Janusz and Rachel had returned to Rachel's apartment courtyard. Janusz drew Rachel towards him and kissed her. "Rachel, dearest. I have something I would like you to have." He opened the flap pocket in his tunic and brought out a small bag with a pull-string top. "I bought this in Warsaw, hoping you would have something of mine while I was away." He opened the bag and drew out a thin silver chain.

"It's beautiful," Rachel whispered as he placed it around her neck.

Janusz smiled and took Rachel into his arms and kissed her. "Now," he said as he stood back, "I must go before I'm listed as a deserter. I love you, Rachel."

"Janusz . . ."

"Shh. Don't talk. I'll come back."

"I love you, Janusz," Rachel whispered.

"After tonight, I don't ever need to be told. When I come back, we'll find some way to resolve the problem with your father. All I ask is that you love me – always."

Rachel threw her arms around him. Tears slid down her cheeks. "Come back," she pleaded. "Please, come back."

Janusz removed her arms from around his neck and gave her a soft kiss. "Count on it," he said as he slowly backed away, taking small steps from her. He blew a kiss, turned quickly and ran from the courtyard. Just then the moon disappeared behind a cloud and the night darkened.

Rachel watched him disappear. "Come back," she whispered. "Please come back to me." She pulled a handkerchief from her purse and wiped her eyes. She had gone beyond the forbidden and only time would tell if she would pay the price. A cool breeze caused her to shiver. She stared out into the darkness one more time, turned and entered the building.

Jonas: The Baker

THE GRAY, SULLEN sky cast a gloom over the assemblage in the small park. The harsh, cold wind forced people to shift from one foot to the other as they attempted to capture the smallest spark of warmth and, even though they hid their mouths behind their scarves and kerchiefs, a steady hum of voices could be heard over the gusting wind. They stood watching, waiting . . . waiting.

Aaron stood among them, shivering, the wind penetrating his many layers of clothing as if he were naked. He stared up at his friend, the baker. He was more than a friend. At sixty-five, Uncle Jonas was gruff with his customers, but was always *shtiping* his small friends with cookies. He was not really Aaron's uncle, but all the boys on Zgierska Street called him uncle because of his genuine interest in their lives and he became a role model of goodness to the many young boys he befriended, boys in need of more than pastry and sweets. Uncle Jonas was never too busy to listen to their problems, however trivial, and dispensed his judgements with the care of a concerned physician. To Aaron, he was a teacher, a mentor and a beacon of compassion. Today, he would become an example.

"Why, Jonas?" Aaron asked under his breath. "You promised. Why didn't you keep your promise?"

Jonas looked down, and their eyes locked. He smiled, a brief smile that disappeared before those who stood beside him could become aware of it.

"Why, Jonas? You always gave me advice that I followed. Why didn't you take mine this time?" He spoke these words in his head, but his eyes pleaded for an answer.

Aaron remembered the time when he was sixteen, looking for a job. After many weeks of rejections and broken promises, Jonas had given him advice. Jonas was leaning against the door of his bakery, munching on a strudel, wearing a vest too small for his broad chest. From his waist to his knees, his apron was decorated with sauces and fruit stain.

"Good morning, Aaron. Do you have time to talk with a bored old man?"

"Good morning, Uncle Jonas. Bored? Yesterday, when I came by, you were so busy I couldn't see you for all the people in your bakery. Today you're bored?"

Jonas beamed as he cleared his throat. "Ah-hem, Aaron, you ask that because you've never owned a business. My business is like the weather. Sunday and Monday it's cold because the bread from *Shabbas* is still plentiful. Tuesday and Wednesday it's hot because the bread is finally gone. Thursday there is a breeze, but Friday . . . *oy vey*!" Jonas looked comical as he acted out his words, his voice fluctuating with the drama of his response. He ended with a hearty laugh, thoroughly enjoying his own theatrics.

Aaron laughed with him.

"So, tell me, Aaron, any luck today?"

Aaron shrugged his disappointment. "No work yet. I had a couple tell me to come back tomorrow. Do you know how many times I've heard that?"

Jonas nodded. "Yes, I know. Aaron, it seems to me, this might be the right time to start your own business."

Aaron showed his surprise. "I'm just a helper. I can help in the vegetable store or in the fish store. I can even help Mr. Kline ship his dresses to his customers outside the district, but I don't know how to make a dress or even skin a fish. I don't like to do those things."

"You want to enjoy your livelihood. That's a lofty ambition. When I was young, we did what we had to because if we didn't, we had nothing."

Aaron gave Jonas a sideways glance that suggested he didn't quite believe what he heard. Then he smiled and asked, "Are you telling me that you don't like being a baker?" He poked his forefinger into Jonas's distended stomach.

Jonas chuckled. "Ahh, I got lucky. Wait. What you need is energy." Jonas took a few steps into the bakery, reached over the counter and retrieved a slice of strudel. He handed it to Aaron. "Here. Enjoy."

Silently, they munched on their strudels, watching the traffic in the street. All types of bicycles skillfully manoeuvred between the many vehicles and horse-drawn wagons that passed, their owners slouched on their high perches, seemingly half-asleep.

"It's almost noon. I should be going," Aaron reluctantly said. "There's still a place where I might find a job and I don't want to lose it because I took too long eating your strudel."

"Ahh-m, that's not true," Jonas answered. "It's not my strudel, it's yours. I gave it to you. The last thing you want to become is a victim of cause and effect."

"Cause and effect? What do you mean?"

"Believing that things go wrong because it is someone's fault. By focusing blame on someone, the effect of what went wrong is lost. Blame no one. Learn from the experience."

Unsure whether Uncle Jonas was serious or joking, Aaron just nodded.

"You could do that, Aaron," Jonas said pointing to the street.

"Be a peddler with a pushcart?" Aaron rolled his eyes.

"It's an honourable profession. I started that way. It's a simple business of mathematics. You buy something for almost nothing, sell it for a little more than nothing and you make something."

Aaron laughed. "Doesn't sound like a business that interests me."

"Does it have to? It's a start. If you make no effort, you must expect nothing."

"I don't think so."

"I built a bakery."

Aaron smiled. "And all from next to nothing."

Jonas's hand suddenly snapped out, pulling Aaron's cap over his eyes. "A-uh! I knew there was a reason for your stubbornness. You're blind."

A GUST OF cold wind struck Aaron and he shivered, pulling his coat closer around him. Jonas was right, he had been blind. Over the years Jonas had opened his eyes and mind to many opportunities. Aaron gazed again at his friend and tears coursed down his cheeks as he watched his friend who stared at the trees he loved and the people who were his friends, waiting . . . waiting.

"Why, Jonas? If only you had not tried to make amends for the past."

It was three years ago that Aaron had learned about New York City. On his way home, he had stopped for bread. The bakery was filled with women clamouring to be served and Jonas was about to explode with frustration. "Mrs. Swartz, for at least fifteen years you have been coming here. For fifteen years, I have heard the same question – 'Is the chalah fresh?' Now, I ask you, why would it not be fresh? It's so fresh, Mrs. Swartz, the inside is still cooking. Why would you think it was not fresh?"

Ethel Swartz was five-feet-two when her hair was fluffed up. With everyone's attention focused on her, she replied, "How do I know it was not baked yesterday?"

"How do you know? Yesterday was Thursday and I only bake chalahs for the Sabbath. I never bake chalahs on Thursday."

"How do I know?"

"Because I say so."

"Uh-huh! Men always lie. I want a fresh chalah."

"Yes, Mrs. Swartz." Jonas rolled his eyes heavenward as if asking for guidance. He reached for a chalah behind him and wrapped it with a sheet of brown paper.

He noticed Aaron and smiled.

"Is the mandelbrot fresh?" Mrs. Swartz asked.

"No, Mrs. Swartz. It was made from old dough. That's why it is hard."

Several customers laughed. Mrs. Swartz did not appreciate Jonas's humour. She fiddled in her purse for the exact amount and paid him. Immediately, the waiting customers clamoured for Jonas's attention. Jonas shouted to Aaron, "I want to talk to you." He pounded his big fist against the wall behind him and the clamour subsided. Jonas smiled at his customers. "I'm calling for my new assistant," he said to the women waiting to be served. "I have to talk to my friend."

All eyes turned to Aaron.

A young man of about fifteen entered from the back room, a large apron wrapped around his waist, flecks of white flour on his face and hands. He approached hesitantly.

"Ladies, this is Hershl Cohen."

All eyes swung to the boy.

"Yes, Mr. Ginzburg?"

"Well, Hershl, I warned you this day would come."

"Yes, sir."

"You will attend to my customers while I talk to my friend."

"Yes, sir."

"Hershl, after you collect the money, it goes into the cash box, not into your pocket. Understood?"

"Yes, sir."

Jonas, a big man, stood over Hershl Cohen and gazed at him fiercely. "God will be watching you. But in case He is distracted, I will be also watching."

"Yes, sir," whispered Hershl Cohen, his eyes round as saucers as they darted from Jonas to the impatient customers.

Aaron followed Jonas into the back room. He watched as Jonas closed the door behind him and collapsed into a large tub chair.

"This business will be the death of me yet," he groaned as he stretched his legs to ease the discomfort of standing for hours.

Aaron laughed. "Tell me, Jonas, what do you do with the bread that is not fresh?"

Jonas smiled. "All bread is fresh, Aaron. It just needs a little fire to bring it back to life. But some I give to Rabbi Sternberg. He knows who would appreciate yesterday's bread."

"And the boy, who is he?"

Jonas grinned. "A hardened criminal."

"Really!"

"An orphan. He broke into Ira Schindler's house and stole a bag of food."

"Only food?"

"A little money."

"What has this to do with you?"

"I'm the jailer."

"How come?"

"Rabbi Sternberg learned of the boy's arrest and persuaded Schindler to drop the charges. I promised to teach the boy how to be a baker."

"Aren't you afraid he will steal your money? You left him alone. Once a thief . . ."

Jonas's expression became solemn. "No, Aaron. He was alone and hungry. Children are not born to steal. They are either taught or have a need without the ability to resolve that need. He stole because he had no other options. No other options that he knew of. No, he won't steal from me. The money is safer than if it were in my own hands. I only acted tough because that was what he expects. But I left him with the money because that will give him cause to think."

Aaron shook his head in amazement and then laughed heartily.

Jonas laughed too. "Aaron, I was hoping I would see you today. You have me worried."

"Why? What have I done?"

"That's good. You're learning. Your face has that look of innocence. God forbid you should show your real feelings. What have you done? I hear you and your friend Gershon still persist in goading gentile bullies and causing fights."

"Who says we goad them? They're looking for a fight and we accommodate. Their trouble is they don't expect us to fight and that's where Gershon and I give them a lesson or two."

"That's bad, Aaron. Gershon's trouble. He feels with his fists. But you, you feel with your heart. You and Gershon cannot change overnight what has been for thousands of years."

"Maybe not, but it's a start. There has to come a time when we must take a stand."

"When you look for trouble, it will find you."

"Do nothing and nothing changes. Putting off for tomorrow only postpones the inevitable. Today is as good a time as any to start."

"You are gifted, Aaron. You can use words to change people's minds. If you continue on your present course, though, others might suffer from your actions. I speak from experience."

Aaron grinned. "You don't strike me as an activist, Jonas."

"I'm not." Jonas smiled weakly.

"Something happened to you?"

"Yes. Thirty years ago in New York City."

"You've been to America?"

"My father and I had a terrible argument. In the larger scheme of things, it was trivial, but then I was a difficult person. He sent me to his brother, who was a baker in New York City. I met a girl there, Sarah. We fell in love, got married and moved in over the bakery. The east side of New York City was a dirty place – filth, criminals and poverty. Like my father, my uncle was a frightened man who cloistered himself in God's protection. His livelihood was the bakery, but his life was the Torah. Gangsters wanted my uncle to pay protection money and I convinced him not to pay. They blew up the bakery with kerosene bombs while I was at the market. The fire ate into the wooden structure and raced to the second floor in minutes. Sarah was upstairs. She was three months pregnant. She died and so did my uncle."

"I'm sorry, Jonas."

"I was responsible for Sarah's death. We are supposed to pay for our own mistakes, but others paid for mine."

"They were gangsters, Jonas. You were right."

"I know. But the price I paid wasn't worth my stand. When I returned to Poland, my father refused to talk to me. I became dead to him. He said I killed his brother. He never knew my Sarah, so she didn't exist for him. Nothing remains the same, Aaron. Changes always occur. There are those who have nothing to lose and they can take risks. Gershon is such a person. You are not."

"You want me to quit what I'm doing?"

"Aaron, Aaron. I want you to understand what you are doing. You have to make the decision. I'm your friend, Aaron. You're like the child I lost. I ask only that you be sure this is really what you want."

"It's not that simple."

"It never is."

Aaron looked confused. "I'll think about it."

Suddenly, there was pounding on the wall. "*Oy*. Must be Hershl. I had better get back. We'll talk about this again."

But they never did. He and Gershon stopped going out at night looking for trouble. Then war came to Poland and life as they knew it came to an end when the Germans arrived and the bigots surfaced. Hate followed greed and the lust for power ruled. One night, not long after Poland surrendered, Jonas knocked on Aaron's apartment door.

"What are you doing here?" Aaron asked.

"I need your help, Aaron. The Germans want me to continue making bread but they told me how many loaves I could bake. No more, no less. Any attempt to bake even one more and I will be punished. They will pre-measure my flour, giving me less than I need. I asked how I was to make more bread from less dough? 'Use more water,' they said. They are idiots."

"How can I help?"

"Last spring, when I realized there might be a war, I secretly, at night, dug a bunker under my back shed. The shed is unheated. I use it to store a broken oven and anything no longer useable. It is an unlikely place for anyone to expect to find a room under the floor."

"What's in the room?"

Jonas smiled. "I started buying extra flour and bagged them in one-kilo containers."

"How many do you have?"

"Eighteen."

"Eighteen! My God, they'll be worth a fortune on the black market."

"No, Aaron. It's for the orphaned children. They have no one but me."

"Of course, I should have known. What can I do?"

Jonas placed both his hands on Aaron's shoulders. "I will bake six extra loaves every day and hide them in the bunker. At night, you remove them and give them to Rabbi Sternberg." He placed one hand in his pocket, removing a small piece of paper with several names. He will give it to these children. Half a loaf is for you."

"Not necessary."

"Yes it is. You'll need your strength to do what I ask."

"I have other sources for getting food, but I'll get someone else for the bread. Someone who needs the bread more than I do. But there's a condition."

"What?"

"Promise me that you will let someone else handle the distribution of the bread. You must not get involved. You will be watched. Bake them, but no more. Do you promise?"

Jonas smiled. "Yes. I promise. I knew I could count on you." He moved to the door. "Do you remember what I said about what happened to me in America? A gangster is a gangster, even if he wears a uniform."

"I remember, Jonas. Just be careful," Aaron said. "We shouldn't see each other again."

"Goodbye, my friend. Until we meet again when this terrible tragedy ends."

WHO COULD HAVE thought it would end like this, in a park, with more than a thousand people watching, all because someone stole the flour from the hiding place. In desperation, Jonas had tried to smuggle two extra loaves of bread from the German's ration to the children and was caught.

Aaron watched a sedan enter the park and stop in front of the platform. A German officer stepped out. He gazed contemptuously at the assembled crowd. He was tall and thin, with a posture that reeked of arrogance and self-importance. Aaron's eyes followed him to the foot of the steps and watched him climb. The officer did not glance at Jonas but stepped to the front of the platform and faced the people.

"Take notice!" he shouted, pointing to Jonas. "That man withheld loaves of bread that were the property of the German government. He claimed they were for the children. The Third Reich has been benevolent and generous to the Jews of this miserable country. We offered you life, in spite of your evil practices, in spite of your desire to dominate the world." He stared at the milling crowd, a snarl on his face. "We generously forgave and hoped you would see the error of your ways, but you flaunted our kindness by defying our rules. Hunger is not an excuse; and disobedience is inexcusable. The penalty is death."

The people stared up at the platform, their white faces numb with grief, their bodies rigid with the shock at the expected news. Jonas continued to stare towards the distant horizon, his eyes focused into space, his lips clenched tightly, waiting . . . waiting.

A hand touched Aaron's shoulder and he snapped his head back. It was Gershon.

"Jonas's way won't work with Nazis," Gershon said. "They're jackals. They will consume everything and never know when to stop."

"I know."

The German officer nodded his head toward a soldier holding a wooden bar attached to a rope, a look of satisfaction crept onto his face. The trap door opened and Jonas's body disappeared momentarily from view. The rope snapped loudly when it was brought up short. Jonas's head twisted unnaturally to the side, his mouth opened and his sightless eyes gazed at the underside of the platform. A collective moan of despair rose from the people as the corpse swung slowly in circles.

Aaron turned away, tears streaming down his face. Idiots, he thought. Idiots! What have they destroyed, a man's body? They cannot destroy what he stood for.

"What now?" said Gershon.

Aaron stared at Gershon. His answer came in a whisper.

"When words fail, it is time to act.

Tell all the boys.

Tell them it's time to make a stand against the gangsters.

Tell them it's a matter of cause and effect.

Tell them to remember Jonas, if they have any doubts."

Promise: Come Home

JACOB RUSHED INTO the house without closing the front door. "Quickly, Hannah, we don't have much time."

Eight-year-old Rachel stood in front of her mother, her coat and hat draped over a small cloth bag at her feet, a look of fear on her face. "Please, Poppa!" she begged. "Please! I don't want to go."

A small face appeared from behind Hannah. It was their nine-year-old son, Gershon, his small hands clutching his mother's dress so hard that the tips of his fingers appeared bloodless.

"Hannah, help me," Jacob pleaded. "We are running out of time. Mr. Volhynia is waiting. We must hurry before he changes his mind."

Hannah gently pushed Rachel forward. "Go," she said softly. "You have to go."

Silently, Rachel's eyes pleaded for her mother to change her mind but her mother slowly shook her head. Rachel picked up the bag and moved towards the door.

"Rachel," her father called. "Remember, never speak Yiddish. Your name is Mary Volhynia, the niece of Alexander Volhynia. You are with them because your father died. It is important that no one know you are a Jew. Never forget."

"Yes, Poppa."

"We love you, Rachel. Always remember that we love you."

"Yes, Poppa."

"Promise me you'll come home when the war is over. No matter where you are . . . come home. Here is where we will leave you a message – if possible."

"I promise, Poppa."

"Go. Be safe."

Rachel turned her back on her family and left the house.

MR. VOLHYNIA, A supplier for Rachel's father's carpentry business, did not look happy. Rachel had to pretend to be his niece because of the Germans. Who were these Germans? Why were they coming to the Ukraine? For weeks she sensed the tension in her house, at school and even in the streets. There was fear in everyone's eyes. As she entered the car, she whispered, "I will come back, Poppa, I promise." Before the car door was closed, the vehicle was moving. She stared out the front window as tears fell from her cheeks.

RACHEL WATCHED FROM the window of Mr. Volhynia's house as her world changed when the Germans came to her city.

She saw violence.

She saw fear.

She even saw death.

Mr. Volhynia was always frightened. He told her that he'd gone by her parent's house, but the house was empty. The broken front door was lying on the steps. Rachel paled with the news and tears silently slid down her cheeks. Mr. Volhynia said he was sorry.

Mr. Volhynia was a man haunted by his fears. His world had also changed. First the Jews disappeared, then the intellectuals, and now the Germans were taking the skilled labourers to Germany to work in labour camps. He was afraid Rachel would be discovered. One day, he took her to live with his cousin in another community. Before curfew he left her in an empty house just outside the city. In the middle of the night, a man came and took her home. The next day they went by horse and wagon to a town a day away, where she stayed. Months later, the cousin took her to Odessa, near the Black Sea, to live with other friends – a fishing family. That didn't last long either. She was taken to Turkey and given to someone else. When the war ended in 1945, she was in Syria. From there, a man took her to the border of Palestine and left her. Until she was old enough to be on her own, she lived in a kibbutz. In time, she became an Israeli, found love, married, had two children and moved to Tel Aviv.

RACHEL CLIMBED THE stairs to her apartment. Her husband, Moishe, was reading a newspaper at the kitchen table. "It must be hot enough to fry an egg on the asphalt," she said.

Moishe smiled. "Better here then in the Ukraine. It's cold there."

Rachel sat on the couch and removed her shoes. "What are you reading?"

"Israel and Ukraine have made up."

"No!"

"It's in the newspaper. Anyone wishing to go need only have a passport and apply for a visa."

Rachel hurried into the kitchen, grabbed the paper and read the article.

"You're not going to go, are you?" he said.

"Moishe, I haven't been home in over fifty years. I was eight when I left; I'm fifty-nine now. Maybe there is a message waiting for me. I promised. I must go back."

"That was a promise made by a little girl."

"Does it matter?"

"Rachel, what you will find are stories of death."

"You don't understand, Moishe. I promised. I have no choice."

"You don't even remember your address. You'll be a Jew in a country that has a history of hating Jews. Who will help you?"

"I have to go, Moishe."

"Not yet. Give me time."

"For what?"

"To figure out how I can help."

"I'll wait, but I'm going."

"I'll need two months to get you some answers that will help you. Once you are there, you will have only yourself to rely on. The less you need others, the safer you will be."

"All right, Moishe. Two months. No longer."

THE TAXI LEFT her standing at the intersection. Rachel looked for a familiar landmark. She had memorized everything Moishe had found out about the city of Rakhiv. She remembered that her parents had owned a carpentry business and lived in a modest, two-storey house on a long street. On the corner was a fruit store, next to it a barbershop and then a tailor shop. There was a *shtibl*, a prayer house, where Jewish men went on the Sabbath to pray. She could see none of these.

Moishe said that the Jews lived in a cluster, rather than a district. She had been to two such streets; there were no Jews left in either. She saw the way people stared at her. She looked at each house she passed, looking for something to trigger a recollection. She walked a couple of blocks in one direction and then returned to where the taxi had left her and walked in the other direction. Many of the houses were less than fifty years old. She could tell. Had her house been one of those destroyed? Was that why nothing looked the same?

She went another block. Her pace slowed, maybe she had gone

too far. She stopped at the corner and looked up an intersecting street and saw they were older homes. She slowly followed that street, stopping in front of a house. She tried to imagine how it might have looked in 1941. Passersby stared at her. Although she was simply dressed, she still stood out. She wanted to ask someone a question, but when she had done that earlier, the man had spit at her. He had recognized that she was Jewish. She saw the hate in his face and it had left her shaken.

She had already spent hours walking, but nothing she had seen was familiar. She stopped in front of another house. Her heart accelerated. She crossed the street and gazed at it for several minutes. A smile crossed her lips. "Yes," she whispered, "Yes."

Rachel knocked on the door. Someone pulled the curtain away from the small window in the door and a woman's face peered at her. Rachel offered a nervous smile. The woman stared hard at Rachel for a few minutes, let the curtain fall and partially opened the door.

"Yes?" the woman said.

In broken Ukrainian, Rachel said, "My name is Rachel. I believe I used to live here." She had memorized what she was going to say. She didn't want the owner to think she was interested in the house as property. She was not there to claim it.

The woman appeared momentarily caught off guard. "This is my house," she stammered. "I bought it many years ago. I have proper papers."

Rachel had difficulty understanding everything the woman said, she spoke so fast. From the tone, Rachel realized she had given her the wrong impression.

"No, no," she answered. "I once lived here. I don't want the house."

The woman's face softened. "I understand. You wish to come inside?" she asked.

"Yes. May I?"

The woman opened the door all the way and waved Rachel in.

Rachel found herself in the living room. The furniture was old but well kept. The house was clean, an aroma of food lingered in the air. She scanned the four walls, then turned to the woman and said, "When you bought the house, were the walls brown?"

"Yes, they were light brown."

Rachel smiled. She had found her home. She pointed to a corner. "There was a cabinet there. My father built it. The left door was broken."

"Yes. I had to get rid of it. It cost too much to repair."

Rachel chuckled, her hand covered her mouth as her eyes widened with her discovery. She moved into the room and her eyes saw, not what was before her, but what had been there before. "Was there a big carpet here? Persian. Red with an intricate pattern," she asked excitedly.

The woman seemed reluctant to answer.

Rachel stared at her curiously. "No?"

"Yes," she said. "It was . . . damaged."

"How?"

The woman looked away. "Blood."

Rachel's smile slipped from her face. "I understand," she said softly.

They walked slowly from one room to another in silence, then to the second floor, down to the basement and back to the front door. Rachel had tears in her eyes. "Thank you. It has meant a lot to me to come here."

The woman saw the tears. "Why did you come?"

"I promised my father I would return one day."

"Why?"

Rachel closed her coat. "I don't know. A hope." She gave a small smile, placing her hand on the door knob. "My father said he would try to leave me a message." Rachel sensed that the woman was struggling to say something. "What is it?" Rachel prompted her.

"I found no letters. The house had been empty for years. But last week, a man came and also asked to see the house. He, too, said he had lived here. He left me a card and asked that if anyone else came to look at the house, would I give that person his card. He does not have the same last name as you. Would you like the card?"

Rachel eyes opened wide. "A man. Here? Yes!"

The woman went up the stairs. When she returned, she held a business card in her hand. With trembling hands, Rachel took the card. On it was her brother Gershon's name and address – *ten kilometres from where she lived in Israel.*

Kugler forced himself through the heavy underbrush, his chest heaving with every breath, his legs aching, his body weak from the many months of hard labour at the camp. Freedom was just a few hills away, if he could only escape from the Germans chasing him. Earlier that morning, he was one of four hundred prisoners who were forced out of Wageningen Labour Camp and made to march to Germany. He was not a prisoner-of-war or a Jew. Wageningen was a camp for Christian political prisoners, thieves, smugglers and enemies of Germany. He fell into the last category.

As they marched, German soldiers shouted at the prisoners to move faster. "*Schnell! Schnell!*" Kugler heard over and over again. Whenever someone faltered, a shot rang out and another body lay by the roadside. "*Schnell!*" If a prisoner dropped to his knees, two exhausted prisoners lifted him to his feet and dragged him forward until he was able to move himself. If he were no longer able to carry his own weight, they would gently lay him by the edge of the road and continue on. Another shot would ring out. Several times, Kugler had assisted in supporting someone. Too often, the end was the same and, with determination, he had struggled on.

The sudden attacks of the American airplanes had made everyone jump into the ditches that lined the road. But Kugler had run instead. As he raced down the incline through the thick brush, shots rang out behind him. The sounds of bombs falling and machine guns firing were deafening. Fear propelled his tired legs to move faster.

Kugler crossed a stream and reentered the forest. Ahead, he saw a dilapidated old farmhouse, partially hidden by trees, and directed his feet towards it. He pushed at the door, but it wouldn't budge. Then he ran around the building looking for an opening, but all the windows had been shuttered and sealed. He tried desperately to lift the cellar door, but it wouldn't move – the door, he realized, had been nailed to the frame. Returning to the front door, he tried the handle again, but there was no movement. Exhausted, he slumped to the ground, his head falling to his chest and closed his eyes. He was thirsty and regretted not having stopped to drink at the stream. And he was hungry. He remembered the two slices of old bread in his pocket that his German captors had given him as his ration for the day before they left the camp. He got to his feet to reach into his pocket when he heard someone whisper, "Go away!"

Kugler edged closer to the door. "Who's there?"

"Go away!"

"Let me in," Kugler begged. "The Germans are following me."

"Are you stupid? You've led them to me. Go away!"

Kugler pushed at the door, but it wouldn't budge. "Don't be afraid. Let me in. I'm a prisoner."

"This is my hiding place," the voice said.

Kugler glanced over his shoulders, fearing the Germans might be near by, and would hear them argue. "Are you hungry? I have bread."

"How much?"

"Enough for both of us. Let me in and I'll share it."

"You had better not be lying." There was the sound of furniture being moved and the door opened. Kugler hurried in and stood by the far wall. The room was dark, almost too dark to see beyond his outstretched hand. The man grunted, tired by his effort to replace the furniture against the door. "Where's the bread?" he demanded.

Kugler reached into his pocket and retrieved the two slices. They were hard. "Here." Kugler extended a single slice.

The man in the shadows snatched the bread from his fingers and moved to the far wall across from Kugler. He slid to the floor.

"Can I stay?" Kugler asked.

"Do what you want, but don't bother me."

Kugler lowered himself to the floor, his back against the wall. "I think it would be better if I stayed here for the night. It's too dangerous to wander around outside in the dark."

"I let you in because I was hungry. I didn't ask to be your friend. Go or stay, I don't care."

"Did you just escape?"

"Are you deaf?"

"Sir, we can't just stare at each other. What harm can there be in talking?"

The man rose to his feet and stood in front of Kugler. "Have you eaten the other slice?"

"No," Kugler said.

"Give it to me. I'm still hungry."

"So am I. This was my breakfast. I saved it for the march. Where's your bread?"

"What difference does that make? I'm still hungry." He raised his voice. "Give me half."

"Lower your voice," Kugler whispered. "The Germans will hear."

The man lowered himself to the floor beside Kugler and extended his hand. Kugler glared at him, broke the slice of bread in two and gave him one. "The one you kept looks bigger," the man said.

"It is. You're lucky I gave you any." Kugler bit into the hard shell and crunched off a piece.

The man settled back and took a bite. "Why were you in prison?" he asked.

"Why were you?"

"Smuggling. You?"

"Nothing of importance," Kugler answered in a low voice.

"Nothing! They don't put people into a labour camp for nothing, unless they're a Jew – and you're not. Wageningen was not a Jewish camp. So why were you at Wageningen?"

Kugler didn't answer.

The man's voice rose in anger. "I asked you a question."

"What I did was insignificant."

"Really! The Germans made a mistake?"

"No."

"Okay," the man said, rising to his feet, "you're playing games. Well, I don't play games. The Germans must have passed by already, so leave. I'd rather be alone anyway."

"I apologize," Kugler said. "It's just that I've never told anyone about what I did, so I find it difficult."

"No one? The Germans must have known what you did, otherwise why would they throw you into prison."

Kugler shook his head in the dark. "Even they don't know what I did, only what they suspect."

"Now I am curious," the man said. "Let's do it this way."

"What?"

"I'll tell you about myself and you tell me about yourself, but we'll talk in general terms – without revealing names." There was a slight pause. "Hey, I'm sorry about my temper, but I'm scared, too. What do you say? Where's the harm?"

Kugler could not make out the man's face in the darkness, but his voice sounded sincere. He mulled over the suggestion, trying to make sense of what it was he had lived with these past three years and the secret he kept.

"Let me start," the man said. "I was in textiles before the war and quite wealthy. And you, what did you do before the war?"

Kugler hesitated before he answered, "I was an employee at a bakery and spice company."

"Where?"

"Amsterdam."

"My business was in Utrecht," the man said.

"I worked there, too," Kugler said, "from 1920 until the new owner bought the business and moved it to Amsterdam in 1933. My wife and I decided to follow him there."

"When the depression hit Holland," the man continued, "our country was flooded with refugees. Many became my competitors, mostly Jews working out of their homes. If I told you that more than 300,000 refugees came from Nazi Germany to Holland to pick the bones of our sick country, you would understand why, when my business failed, I turned to smuggling. Liquor. In times of war, people's values change and the unacceptable becomes acceptable. It was never my intention to do this permanently, I want you to know, but the demand was great and I had access to the demand." He paused. "Anyway, who asked those refugees to come to Holland? If they'd gone elsewhere, the Germans might have left us alone. Who told them to come here and take what was not theirs?"

"My employer was from Germany," Kugler said softly.

"He was?"

"He had new ideas and different ways of doing business. He was aggressive in his selling. He created new products and a new image. At first it took a little getting used to, for my ways were more traditional. But the company grew and prospered. The employees depended on him and he on them."

"Really," the man said, the tone of his voice indicating he wasn't pleased at having his point of view contradicted. He paused, and then asked, "You have a slight accent. You aren't Dutch, are you?"

"No, Austrian. I fought in the Imperial Navy during the First World War and then came to Holland."

"I see," the man said.

"I get the impression you are all about money." Kugler's tone challenged the man.

"What does that mean? In this world you take what you can or it will be taken from you. You said your employer's company prospered. You were probably a major factor in that prosperity. Did he share any of it with you?"

"In his way, yes. I was the administrator. My responsibility was to make sure the factory and office ran smoothly and that the accounts reflected the proper records. I enjoyed my responsibility. It gave me a great deal of satisfaction and he compensated me with a fair wage."

"I'm impressed. Your personal needs must be simple. I could have used you in my textile business," the man said. "My employees robbed me blind. I went bankrupt because they couldn't produce the work at the price I needed to make a profit."

"My employer paid a decent wage and everyone appreciated the way they were treated. There was a good deal of mutual respect, I believe, and he still made a profit. I can see you were more concerned with profit than people."

The man gave a short laugh. "Profits are generated by minimizing expenses and wages are an expense."

Kugler clenched his fists in the darkness. "My employer treated us with respect," he said. "His pain became ours. When the Germans came, his life was in jeopardy and we helped."

"His life was in jeopardy! Are you saying he was a Jew?" the man exclaimed. "By God, why risk your life to save a Jew?"

The darkness hid Kugler's growing anger. "Why, because I am a Christian? My employer was in danger – not only he, but also his wife and two daughters. How, as a Christian, could I ignore their plight? How could I walk away when it was apparent that my help was essential in saving their lives?"

"Calm down. You were under no obligation to risk your own life to save them. You were lucky the Germans didn't hang you when they caught you. Jews!"

Kugler sprang to his feet. "I never thought about the risk to my own life. I had a duty to try to save theirs. You talk of profit – I tell you of need. You refer to my actions as foolish, but I think yours were selfish. Not everything we do is supposed to add to our financial wealth. I'm not a Christian because I was born one! I believe in the teachings of Christ."

"Shh, shh. Sorry. Sit. Please. And keep your voice down."

Kugler lowered himself to the floor. There was silence as both allowed the tension to dissipate. At last Kugler spoke. "The Germans were rounding up all the Jews. Being Jewish was not a crime in my eyes. I went to him with a plan which he agreed to and we enlisted the help of others in the company."

"That's amazing. But your plan was doomed to fail. All Jews had their assets confiscated," the man said.

"He had no listed assets. Before the Germans came, he had transferred ownership of his business to a Christian not associated directly with the company."

"Another flaw in your plan," the man said. "Your weakness was too many conspirators. You opened yourself to more chances of discovery. Your plan was doomed."

Kugler grinned. "Not so. The plan called for them to be hidden in our warehouse: a large building with three floors overlooking the canal. The warehouse and plant were on the first floor, the main offices and the showroom on the second. On the third floor were two doors: the left took you to the spice-storage area at the front of the building and the right door to an annexe, a large area with a low ceiling and many rooms that extended to the back of the warehouse. This space was the laboratory where I experimented with some of our products and it had toilet facilities and a sink. The plan was to move my employer's family in stages over a couple of months, with enough furniture for possibly two families."

"Two families? I thought you said only your employer's family. How many people were you hiding?"

"At first seven. Then we had an eighth."

"Eight! My God, eight!"

"Once the families were inside, we built a bookcase on hinges in front of the right door. Anyone coming up the steps would see only one visible door; never realizing that behind the bookcase was a floor that extended farther back. For almost two months, at night, we brought furniture from my employer's apartment to the annexe. Everything fell neatly into place until my employer was told his oldest daughter was on a list to report to the Gestapo. We had to speed up the process."

"Of course. The Germans were sending the Jews to concentration camps. Everyone knew that."

"Yes, but the Germans were also looking for Jews in hiding. Not all of the 160,000 in Holland registered. Still the stigma of the company being once owned by a Jew remained. The Germans came often to look over the building. We were under scrutiny. The Germans wanted all the Jews and it was now necessary to prove you weren't a Jew. The question was who was a Jew?"

"That's a ridiculous question. A Jew is a Jew."

"Really? As I understand it, about 15,000 had only one parent who was Jewish. That makes their child a half-Jew. About 5,000 had only one grandparent that was Jewish. That makes their child a quarter-Jew. Think what that meant. If a quarter-Jew was deemed Jewish, then a three-quarter Christian was a Jew. Even if they were Protestant, Roman Catholic, Anglican or anything, the faith practised was not a refuge from this anti-Jewish law."

"I never thought about it that way."

They heard the sound of a dog barking in the distance and both men froze. Their rapid breathing broke the silence in the room. The man stood and moved to the window, placing himself against the edge where glass and wood met. Kugler stared at his outline, his heart racing. The dog barked again, closer.

"What do you see?" Kugler whispered.

"Shhh."

Each second seemed like an eternity. The dog barked again several times in quick succession, but this time he was farther away. The man returned to his place and sat. "Sound carries. I don't believe the dog was near. Where were you . . .?"

"The Germans introduced the yellow star. We knew we had run

out of time. Then the Germans imposed a curfew against the Jews and we had to move our schedule ahead. Before the rooms were ready, my employer's family of four moved into the annexe; the other family followed a few days later. We told people that our employer and his family had left Amsterdam. Others had left and so their absence was accepted. The plan was moving ahead successfully."

"I see too many flaws. Too much to overcome."

"Such as?"

"Money."

"I managed the company. From the profits, we bought ration cards on the black market. And people helped. The baker must have realized what we were doing, for he would give us more than we were allowed and he never asked for the extra money. The grocer would leave a bag at the door every day and never ask for money either. How many helped, I can't even begin to know, but we were not alone. Money was not the problem, but you are right, there were problems. Thin walls separating the buildings. Sounds carried. If we could hear others, they could hear my employer's family. That meant activities in the annexe had to be minimal during business hours and even at night, for we couldn't be sure that the company next to us didn't have employees working late. Sickness was another problem. The simple act of coughing could mean detection. We feared the common cold as much as a fatal disease. And boredom. Idleness can lead to frustration and anger – anger to shouts. We had to make repairs to the roof. We had to hire new employees we didn't know. Then the owner sold our building. Finally, and the most unlikely, someone broke in one night to rob the warehouse."

"Why would someone break into a spice factory?" The man laughed uncomfortably.

"Who knows, but the next morning, we discovered the back door was broken. We fixed it and said nothing. We couldn't tell the police. But we began to worry. Nothing was missing, so why break in? Did he leave because he heard the children?"

"Your plan was madness."

"No, never madness. Desperation maybe, but not madness."

"You're overly sensitive to criticism, aren't you? You were just lucky."

"Luck had nothing to do with it."

"Oh, no? Luck has everything to do with it. I was caught because my luck ran out."

"How?" Kugler asked.

"At first, I smuggled liquor in from Belgium and France. When that proved too risky, I broke into the homes of wealthy dignitaries, preferably those who were not German. But that too proved dangerous. Then I was forced to . . ." He hesitated.

"Yes?"

"Find liquor elsewhere."

"And?"

"And that was when I got caught. While leaving a place I broke into, the police caught me. A fluke! I was arrested and sent to Wageningen."

"That is indeed strange," Kugler said.

"Why?"

"Smuggling is a firing-squad offence."

"Well . . . with the war lost, they sent me to a camp instead." He quickly changed the subject. "Tell me, how many children were there in these two families?"

"Three; two girls and a boy. One was different though."

"What do you mean, different? Deformed?"

Kugler grinned. "Hardly. Even though she was only a child, she appeared to be blessed with an insight and maturity I have never seen in anyone so young before."

"What do you mean?"

"It's not easy to explain. She looked so fragile, but she had such strength. Not physical, but of mind and conviction. She was only five-feet-two, and not as smart or as attractive as her sister, but she had a sort of mystical radiance. Her eyes were like saucers. They were the eyes of someone who is wise and has understanding beyond her years. Anne was not your usual child."

"Please, no names," the man said, his voice rising slightly to show his displeasure.

"I'm sorry. A slip." Kugler cleared his throat. "She had gray-green eyes and was very candid. She could be capricious, and sometimes unpredictable, but never vicious. Once my wife and I were talking to her when, in mid-sentence, she became quiet and stared at us intently. We wondered why she had stopped talking and was staring at us. Suddenly she said, 'Now I have been talking to your wife and no one heard us.' She had continued our conversation in her head and believed we had been able to hear her. Her eyes conveyed her words with such conviction that it was hard not to believe her sincerity." Kugler gave a short laugh. "Yes, a special child."

Several shots rang out in quick succession. The man jumped to his feet and moved to the window. More shots rang out. Closer.

"This sounds bad," he said. "Someone is being chased nearby. If the Germans see the house, they'll come to see if anyone is inside."

"Should we leave?" Kugler asked.

The man didn't answer right away. "No. We might run right into them. Better we stay put."

The repeated sound of a machine gun was heard, but the echo appeared to be farther away. "They got him," the man said. "The machine gun is for short distances. Whoever they were after is dead." He stood by the window for ten minutes more before returning to his place. "The war is almost over. Everyone knows that and yet the Germans keep killing as if they were victorious. Madness. Sheer madness."

"On that I agree with you," Kugler said.

They sat.

"Continue."

"Another problem was that the two families were both rigid in their ways. Under normal living conditions they got along well but, in confinement, there were displays of temper and a good deal of pettiness. Their old world was gone and this new world required new rules, which they all resented. But not the little girl. She receded into herself and lived for her journal. In it she recorded everything: her thoughts and all that happened in the annexe. She observed, but did not let herself be drawn into the pettiness that was going on around her. She just wrote in her journal."

"What do you mean, a journal?"

"She wrote in a diary. When the journal was filled, she wrote in an unused company ledger book. We all knew she wrote about the two families and about us, the employees who were part of the conspiracy."

"She put your name in a book? That was dangerous. If they were caught, you would be identified." He spoke without conviction.

Kugler smiled. "She gave all of us new names. We were never identified by our real names. And if we were caught, it would make no difference if our names were in her book or not. It would be obvious that we had known what was happening, especially me. I was in charge of the factory and the employees." Kugler could sense that the man was getting bored.

"Interesting, but so what," the man said. "Many children write in diaries."

"True. But she wrote about her feelings. Instead of seeing only the monotony of life in the annexe, she created a world that revealed the inner lives of herself and her fellow prisoners. Occasionally she would read us something from her pages. It was as if she were somewhere else. Picture someone on a deserted island in the Pacific Ocean where every day was a repeat of the day before. Not for her. She could see that each day, in reality, was different. I prayed that God in his wisdom would see to her survival.

"Then came the day that the Gestapo showed up. It was not an accident. Someone had told them." Kugler sighed. "For twenty-six months we had kept the secret and now it had come to an end. It was such a fine summer day. A staff sergeant of the Green Police and three Dutch civilians entered my office and asked to see the owner of the building. I gave them his name and address.

"'No,' they said. 'We want the person who is in charge here.'

"'That is myself,' I replied.

"'Then come along,' they ordered.

"The police wanted to see the storerooms on the third floor. All will be well if they don't want to see anything else, I thought. But after the sergeant had looked at everything, he went out into the corridor, ordering me to come along. At the end of the corridor they all drew their revolvers and the sergeant turned to me.

"'Push aside the bookcase at the head of the corridor,' he said. 'And open the door behind it.'

"'But there's only a bookcase there!' I said.

"At that he turned nasty, for he knew everything. He took hold of the bookcase and pulled; it yielded and the secret door was exposed. He forced me up the narrow steps and I could feel his pistol in my back. As I entered the annexe, I could see my employer's wife standing at the table. With great effort I managed to say, 'The Gestapo is here.'

"She did not start in fright, or say anything at all. All of them seemed utterly calm. The sergeant ordered them to pack their things.

"Because it was lunchtime, I asked the sergeant if I could bring my sandwiches up from my office to eat. He said I could, so I went down to fetch my lunch. One of the staff was sobbing and another sat at his desk, staring into space. I noticed that the front door stood open and I was on the point of going out into the street when I saw another policeman. So I went back upstairs and ate my lunch in my employer's old office, while a policeman stood there pointing a gun at me.

"They ushered the male employee who was part of our conspiracy into the office and the Green police began to interrogate us. 'We have nothing to say to you,' I told them. 'All right, then, you'll come along too,' the policeman replied.

"The ten of us were taken from the building and put in jail. My co-worker and I were separated from the families and then he was released because he was ill. I was sent to Amersfort, then to Zwolle and finally to Wageningen. I never found out what happened to my employer's family or the others in the annexe. I don't know what happened to the youngest daughter. Her journal was probably destroyed."

Kugler's voice had become hoarse. The weight of his story had tired him out. He waited for the man to speak but he said nothing. All he heard was steady breathing. Could he have fallen asleep? How long have I been talking to myself, he wondered. He sighed, made himself comfortable and closed his eyes. Suddenly, he sat bolt upright and stared at the silhouette of the man. All this time the darkened room had obscured the man's face. He had no idea what he looked like, but he understood his behaviour. He said he had been a liquor smuggler. There was a liquor warehouse that had been broken into near their building the night they had been broken into. He leaned back and closed his weary eyes again. He would ask the man in the morning about that, he thought. Then he would see what his unknown companion looked like in the light of day. Sleep overtook him and the rest of the night passed without further incident.

When he awoke, he pushed himself up, feeling discomfort in his back from the position he'd slept in. He scrambled to his feet and saw that the door was open. His companion was gone. Cautiously he left the house and scanned the area as far as the trees would allow. No one was in sight.

He had to go. He shook his head to clear his thoughts and walked towards the trees. Then he stopped and stared into the sky.

"God, did you save Anne?"

The birds sang and the trees swayed gently in the wind. Victor Kugler listened to the sounds around him for a few minutes then turned and scurried into the forest.

Epilogue

This story is fiction but the facts are true. Victor Kugler conceived and implemented the plan to hide the Frank family in Amsterdam, Holland during the Second World War. He was the only one of eight conspirators sent to prison – a concentration camp. He escaped near the end of the war and hid in a house in a forest until the retreating Germans passed, and then made his way to a safe city. He didn't find out what happened to the Frank family until much later, when he no longer lived in Europe. In 1948, Victor Kugler immigrated to Canada where he lived out his life as a man of good conscience, modest and shunning notoriety.

There were two popular theories about the person who revealed to the police where the Frank family were hidden; he was either the criminal who broke into the warehouse (there was a break-in) or a new employee who profited from the information. To this day, that person has never been identified.

Victor Kugler, a Righteous Gentile, died on December 16, 1981 at the age of 81 and was buried at Riverside Cemeteries in Toronto, Ontario, Canada.

"Whosoever preserves a single soul,
it is as if he preserved the whole world."

ANGRY WORDS FLEW from the old man's lips, sharp, bitter words of recrimination and hurt. He was a Holocaust survivor. He had lived through a terrible ordeal. Why did his only son not understand his pain? "You're a Jew!" he shouted. "Doesn't that mean anything to you?"

"Enough!" his son shouted back. "Leave it alone."

"Leave it alone?" The old man's voice trembled with passion. "Never! I brought you up as my father would have brought me up. Six million died so you could live. Don't you care?"

"You care enough for the two of us," his son answered. "I've had this crap up to my ears. I don't want your guilt. You live with ghosts and want me to inherit them. I want my own life."

"I was a child when the war came. A child. You have no idea what it's like to be in a concentration camp."

"Yes! I've been hearing about it since the day I was born. I don't want to hear any more."

The old man glowered at his son. "If you don't want to hear any more, then leave. Leave this house. Maybe if you went to Israel, you would discover who you are, discover your roots."

"I am not a tree," his son cried in exasperation. "I was not planted. I don't know who I am. I only know who you are and your life has no room for anything but your grief. The two glared at each other, neither prepared to give an inch. "I have no feelings for you – no love, only pity," the son added and he climbed the stairs to his room.

"Love," the old man called after him. "What do you know of love? I lost the family I loved. What did you lose? I'll tell you what you lost – my respect."

His son's bedroom door slammed.

As he always did when he was troubled, the old man went to his synagogue, to sit alone and ask why had he survived while others more worthy had died? When he returned home, his son was gone. His clothes and some photographs – gone. Aaron had left no message.

AARON LIVED AWAY from his community and joined several groups with different ideologies, trying to find himself in their teachings. But, in the end, he saw nothing but confusion, no peace of mind, no comfort of heart, and worse, no understanding of who he was. Years passed; troubled years, years in which he avoided his father. He was not alone in his confusion and like many others he searched for an answer to his life. He decided to go to India.

AARON'S FATHER ALSO searched. Many nights, the old man stood in Aaron's room and wept. He asked God how had he failed as a father. He searched his thoughts, wanting desperately to make peace with himself. But God did not answer.

AARON JOURNEYED TO New Delhi and joined a cult. He learned words that spoke of other ways and scoffed at his earlier way of life. He gave up material things; he beggared himself, wanting desperately to feel that what he was doing was right. But he didn't know what it was he sought. After a year he left the cult and became an English tutor for children of the wealthy. He built a new life. Time became his friend, for the more time that passed, the more he hoped he could forget.

BUT TIME BECAME the father's enemy. His health declined. He had found the answers to his questions but they had come slowly. Friends were going to Israel and he asked if they would take him. They did. At the Western Wall, he leaned his sick body against the stones and prayed. He felt God's presence for the first time in a long time. He grieved for his son and hoped one day his son would understand as he himself now understood.

ONE DAY, AARON reached for the telephone and dialed the number of one of his father's closest friends.

"Aaron!" The man said in surprise. "Aaron, this is you?"

"Yes. It's been a long time. How are you?"

"I am fine. Where are you calling from? Are you in the city?"

"No, I'm calling from India."

"Is that where you went? It was unfortunate about you and your father. He missed you."

"Things happen," Aaron said.

The man's voice saddened. "Yes, things happen."

"How . . . how is my father?"

There was a long pause, but when he finally spoke, it was very softly. "He's dead, Aaron. It happened last year in Israel. He had a heart attack and never recovered."

Aaron was silent.

"I'm sorry, Aaron. No one knew where to contact you. All your father's things and property are being taken care of by his lawyer."

"What was my father doing in Israel? He hated flying."

"He wasn't well. He wanted to go to Israel at least once before he died. Some friends took him. He made it to the Wall, then he died." Again there was a long pause. "I am sorry," he said again.

Aaron felt great emptiness in him. "Where is he buried?"

"Outside Jerusalem. They thought he would want that, to be buried in a land he cherished. He changed after you left, Aaron. Time changes us all. He loved you, you know. He just didn't know how to tell you. There was a lot of pain in him and he didn't know how to live with it."

"Thank you," Aaron said. He replaced the receiver in its cradle and stared at it for a long, long time. There was much sadness in him, but no tears. He could not change what had happened. He went to his dresser and removed the single snapshot of his father that he had carried with him all these years. He looked at the tired, old face with the grieving eyes, then went to the telephone and dialed the airport.

AARON STOOD ON the hill looking down at the Western Wall, the Temple Wall, a Wall that had witnessed thousands of years of tyranny, of slavery and abuse. He came to the Wall because it was the last place his father had been. He was tempted to touch it, but could not take that first step toward the entrance. He just watched the people below.

"Can I help you?" a fragile voice asked.

Aaron turned. An old man stood beside him, smiling.

"You look lost," the old man said, "so I came over to help. Can I help, young man?"

"No, thank you, Rabbi. I'm all right."

The old man chuckled. "I am not a Rabbi. I'm a Jew performing a *mitzvah* – a good deed. I have been blessed. I survived the Holocaust. I met a good woman, had children and they have blessed me with grandchildren. What more could I ask but to repay God for his kindness?"

Aaron looked at the old man curiously. "And what is it you do that is a *mitzvah?*"

"Most come here for one of two reasons. Some to communicate with God; others to leave a message for someone – a thought left unsaid, a regret never uttered, a confirmation of affection. What better way than with a piece of paper and a pencil. You may ask, why a pencil? Because ink fades over time and lead lasts forever. Sometimes it takes a while for the message to reach the sender. I have been doing this for many years. I sense, young man, that what you need is the paper and the pencil."

Aaron looked at the old man's outstretched hand and saw he held a small sheet of white paper and the stub of a pencil.

"If you are wondering about the size of the pencil, it need only be big enough to put down what you feel." He looked at Aaron with eyes of compassion and gestured that he take what he offered.

"It's too late. The receiver is dead," Aaron said.

"The answer is already waiting for you. It begs for a question so you can understand the answer. I know."

Aaron took the old man's gift, entered the sacred area and moved into a vacated spot. He stared at the stones, trying to find the words he wanted to write. Finally he scribbled his short message on the paper. He rolled the paper until it was no larger than a cigarette and tucked it high above his head in a crack in the stone. With a heavy heart, he returned to the entrance. The old man was no longer there.

FINALLY, HE VISITED his father's gravesite. He had deliberately put off going there. Aaron walked slowly on the path into the cemetery, reluctant to close the distance between the many years that had divided him from his father. What words could he speak to heal the pain that had been inflicted? It was too late for reconciliation, too late for apology. What compelled him to come? Nothing would change.

He followed the instructions given him by the groundskeeper and stopped behind a stone that was his father's. There were so many things he wished he had said, for he now understood what haunted his father. It was the loss of those he loved and the knowledge that he could never tell them of his love. And who was he? He was Aaron Shapiro, loved by an old man whose pain prevented him from declaring his love – a love he now knew existed. Would the harsh words he said when he left haunt him as his father's memory had haunted him? He thought of the note he'd left at the Wall:

To my father:
Forgive Me. I love You.
Aaron

He moved to the front of the monument and read his father's full name, date of birth and death. He read the words inscribed beneath and fell to his knees and wept. Etched in the stone was a quotation:

"those who want to be forgiven must learn to forgive."

I Am A Jew

From the beginning of my life, I did learn,
That I was a Jew and within me did burn,
The desire to know from where I came,
And if my life would be filled with pain.

As the days and years passed, my questions grew.
I searched through books, looking for a clue.
There were lots to read, but nothing I came upon,
That gave me the feeling that I did belong.

A Jew I was born . . . a Jew I could stay.
But what is a Jew that cannot live his way?
Only when I understood what made Israel a nation,
Did I realize the need to continue our creation.

Jerusalem, the city of David and Solomon the Wise.
A city filled with tradition, of pain and cries.
A place where I can find who I am at last.
Where with every step, I can discover my past.

I stand before the Second Temple known as the Western Wall.
My hand caresses the stones as to my knees I fall.
My eyes fill with tears for the remorse and grief
For those millions of Jews who died for their belief.

They will never stand here in front of this place,
And be filled with pride for the Jewish race.
The uniting of Jerusalem – the creating of a State,
A country where Jews can live without hate.

There is pride in my step; my back is straight.
I have found myself, I can now relate.
No longer do I ask – who am I?
For I am a Jew until the day I die.

A home to stay after two thousand years away,
To talk and walk and be able to pray.
I am a Jew; I can touch my past.
I have returned; I am home at last.

Alvin Abram

The Eugene Joseph Story

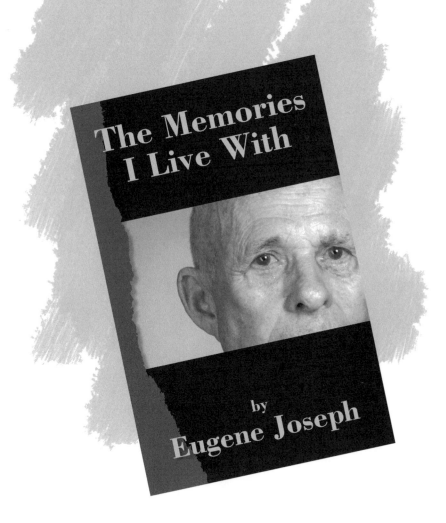

Before me are blank sheets of paper and I struggle to undertake a task that my children have wanted me to do for many years. I feel the need to put down what I have experienced. I want to explain who I am, what I saw; especially the horrors of the Holocaust. I see every aspect of my life clearly in my thoughts and yet I don't know where to begin to record them. It seems so easy but the challenge appears as an impenetrable obstacle. The route, I know, will not be easy. There will be a good deal of pain. Hidden pitfalls that could open memories better left buried and yet there is this urge to record events as I remember them. Why do I want to do this?

I am a Holocaust survivor. I have been told that survivors suffer from guilt. What guilt? What was it I did that I should be guilty of? Surviving? I survived a horrible period in Jewish history and I have been left with memories that haunt me and deeds that may not be understood. I have built walls around many of my thoughts, but cracks are appearing as I grow old and I find myself with questions that seem to have no answers.

Why did I survive?

Was there a purpose?

Was my life meant for something that has yet to happen?

Maybe there are no answers. Maybe what happened just happened. Could it be as simple as that? I was a child when the war came to Hungary. What does a child know of war? Some claim they survived because they were lucky. My luck was my father. He saved my life. Not once but several times and yet I feel nothing for him. Nothing.

I have a story. Is my story different from others? I don't know. I believe my story begins at the end. Even that is strange. I travelled to Israel, a land of hope and dreams, in 1972 for the first time. Many survivors have come here to see if what they had experienced was for this, a place for Jews. I came to see my sister and to visit the grave of my father. The twelve-hour flight was an eternity of memories, a time to reflect, to organize my thoughts, to try to purge my heart. What are memories but the invisible baggage of life? Mine contained a sequence of events in which my father played a main role. I had not seen my father since 1947. Without telling him goodbye, I left him. I ran. I fled. I fled from the memories that fled with me. And now, twenty-five years later, I was making the long trip to where he was buried. For what reason? To look at a mound of earth? Definitely not to ask his forgiveness.

I have a story and I would like to tell it.

THE BEGINNING

I WAS BORN on March 9, 1930, in a small Romanian peasant village named Apahida on the outskirts of Cluj-Napoca, the capital of Transylvania. In 1881, Romania declared itself a kingdom. During the Great War, Romania invaded Hungarian Transylvania, was defeated, re-entered the war and occupied Transylvania and other territories, assuming sovereignty over 51,146 square miles of the Balkan Peninsula, bounded on the north and east by Ukraine, Moldovia and the Black Sea, on the west by Hungary, Croatia and Yugoslavia and on the south by Bulgaria. The Transylvanian Basin, which occupies western Romania, is part of the Carpathian Mountains, with its wide valleys and extensive arable slopes. The most important river is the Danube, which separates Yugoslavia and, for the most part, Bulgaria. Its capital is Bucharest. Approximately 70 percent of the population were Orthodox Christians, 9 percent were Roman Catholics and the balance Jews, Muslims and Gypsies.

When I was born, my parents lived with my mother's parents in a single-room mud hut with mud flooring and homemade furniture. Our village was in an area in which the majority of the residents were Hungarians. Many years ago, this part of the country was part of the Austro-Hungarian Empire and many families established roots in what later became Romania. My native tongue was Hungarian.

My father's name was Moritz, my mother's Miriam. I had two older sisters, Lili, the oldest, and Sari. My grandfather was the village cobbler, my father the village tailor. My father was a good-looking man of average height and weight. He wore his hair combed straight back and had a full moustache and firm jaws. He was also an angry man, often at me, and expressed his anger physically. My mother was a sad, thin woman, with black hair pulled back and a small wave over her right eye. She dressed very plainly.

Life was hard, lonely and not very rewarding. There was only one other Jewish family in Apahida, the grocer's. My grandfather and father had to walk twenty kilometres to the market to sell their goods and buy their material.

When I was three, we moved to Cluj-Napoca, a modern city of pavement and cobblestone streets, wide boulevards, trees, parkland and industry; tall buildings, churches, and houses of one, two and three floors. The population was grouped in clusters, different ethnic religions lived in their own environment. The predominant form of transportation was still the horse and wagon, but automobiles, although rare, were becoming more plentiful with each year and buses were being used to move the population. To a three-year-old, the town was the centre of the universe.

We lived in a single-room flat overlooking a courtyard for four years. Our one room served as kitchen, bedroom and tailor shop. When I was seven, we moved again, this time to a flat in a two-flat complex on the outskirts of the city. Now we had a bedroom, a large kitchen and a large verandah running the whole length of the two flats, as well as a storage area and a woodshed. My mother and father slept in one bed, Lili, Sari and I in another. My sisters slept with their heads at the head of the bed and I slept with my head at the foot, on a mattress made from flour sacks sewn together and stuffed with straw which had to be changed at least twice a year because the straw broke down into powder.

My father bought a second sewing machine and a new, very large cutting table that doubled as the dining table. He bought large scissors that enabled him to cut as many as four layers of cloth at once. The quality of our lives improved.

At this time, I attended the same school as my sisters and had finished grades one and two. It was a government school and almost all the students were of the Christian faith. I integrated well and made friends. I looked like everyone else and being a Jew was not an issue as long as I didn't look like one.

There were many markets in the city. Near our home was Hay Market. Twice a week peasants from nearby Hungarian as well as Romanian villages brought goats, geese, chickens, pigs, straw goods and pottery to sell or barter. Gypsy caravans would set up between market days, but mostly the market was a children's playground, as was the nearby river where we swam and fished. For the two years I went to government school, I was one of them. Them being the Christians. The following year that all changed.

It bothered my father that his only son did not attend a Jewish parochial school. He scraped together enough money to enroll me in a Jewish school and had me grow my side locks long and wear a yarmulke. I was given a new pair of shoes, new clothes, socks and a leather case. This made my sisters envious and our relationship, which was far from close, got worse.

Life at the parochial school wasn't bad. A major difficulty was that I couldn't speak Yiddish. When the other boys wanted to exclude me, they would switch from Romanian to Yiddish. This didn't bother me as much as what happened when I went to play with my old Christian friends. I experienced my first touch of anti-Semitism. I became the "little Jew." My skull cap was always snatched from my head and passed around as I charged after it. The taunting eventually stopped, but not the name. I was always the "little Jew."

My father was a strict disciplinarian, rigid in his interpretation of what went on about him. He never showed me any affection and, in hindsight, I believe he never understood love. Not the giving and not the receiving. As a parent, I have tried to make my children and grandchildren aware of my feelings for them. As a child, I didn't know what it meant; didn't feel it or find comfort in it.

In 1938, European Jewry suffered greatly from Kristallnacht. It was the beginning of change – a change for the worse. For me it was May 1939, during a minor Jewish holy day, that my life changed. I was nine when an incident with my father made me aware that discipline, not love, connected us. My parochial school was closed. My two sisters were getting ready to go to their school when my father realized I wasn't doing the same thing.

"Why are you not getting ready for school?" he asked.

"There is no school today," I answered.

"He's lying," Sari piped up. "He just wants to skip school today."

Lili was quick to confirm what Sari said.

My father had what can best be described as a fit. He removed his belt and repeatedly struck me. My mother succeeded in calming him and he stopped. He ordered me to dress, handed me my bag with the books and told me to go to school without breakfast. As I was leaving, he warned me that he would deal with me and my lying when I returned.

I left the house in pain, humiliated by the injustice. I decided to run away – to where my mother's parents lived, in Apahida, twenty kilometres away. I dumped my books in a ditch and began my trek. I had walked for ten kilometres before I got a ride in a one-horse carriage with an elderly Jewish couple returning to Dej, a small city about fifty kilometres from Cluj-Napoca. On the spur of the moment, I told them I was going to the home of my father's parents in Ileandra Mare, about one hundred kilometres from Cluj-Napoca in the Carpathian Mountains. I said my mother was very sick in the hospital and I was going to my grandparents to get money for doctors and medication. They believed me and I found myself on a journey far beyond anything I had envisioned. I was planning to go farther alone than I had ever gone with my parents, and with strangers, at a time when telephones were rare, when going just twenty kilometres was a journey that took a day. I was nine years old, filled with anger and determined never to return to my father's house.

When we arrived at Dej, they invited me to their home, where I was fed and washed. They let me sleep that night in a spare bedroom and, when I awoke, their maid had cleaned my boots. They gave me a breakfast of white bread, cheese and milk. Such luxury! At home we ate only cheap black bread. They gave me a satchel of food and made arrangement with an open freight wagon to take me to my destination.

I had never been there before, so I went to a grocery store to inquire where my grandparents lived. I was to find out there were many Jozsefs living in the village. This was a community of 2,000, of whom about 500 were Jewish. I spoke Romanian and the people spoke in Yiddish and Romanian. I still didn't understand Yiddish and a crowd formed around me as everyone started asking me questions, such as who I was, how I had gotten here and why I'd come. Then a woman asked what my father's first name was. When I told her, she said, "Oh, that Jozsef?"

Then she and another woman took me to my grandparents, two kilometres outside the village. I told them my parents were poor and had sent me to my grandparents because they could not afford to keep me. Poverty they understood.

My grandparents' house was in a deep and narrow valley. It was no more than a two-room, whitewashed adobe building with a hard-packed dirt floor and a tattered roof. When we walked into the kitchen, which was where the only entrance was, it took a little while to adjust to the semi-darkness. I found it strange that the women didn't knock but just strolled right in. My grandmother was sitting at the table on a homemade stool holding a piece of Johnnycake and sipping something from an earthenware jug. My grandfather stood at the other end of the table, davening, rocking back and forth, an open prayer book from the Talmud before him, turning pages as he said his evening prayers, his prayer shawl draped across his shoulders.

The women told them about me. This led to some confusion. My grandfather was one hundred years old and my grandmother, his third wife was seventy-eight. The confusion was which of his children I belonged to. He had had three sons and one daughter in three marriages. The two women spoke in Yiddish, repeating themselves often. My grandmother was hard of hearing and my grandfather had been blind for over twenty years. He knew his prayers so well that he turned the pages of his book as if he were reading. They finally identified which son my father was.

After the women left, my grandfather addressed me in Yiddish. I answered in Romanian. After a short conversation, he realized that Romanian was not my first language and so he talked to me in Hungarian, which I understood. He told me to come to him. Using his hands, he felt for the yarmulke, which he removed, then the close-cropped hair, the sideburn ringlets, which he pulled straight with his fingers so he could determine how long they were, then my arm, shoulders and body, all the way down to my feet. Satisfied, he told my grandmother that I was a healthy little boy.

A bed was made for me in the kitchen. The next morning, I read out loud from a prayer book so my grandfather could hear how well I knew my prayers. I read fairly fluently, but the prayer was in Hebrew and, like Yiddish, I didn't understand a word I said. He corrected my pronunciation and manner of delivery occasionally, but I could tell he was pleased with what he heard. Throughout the day many visitors came to see the little boy from the big city, to hear the story of how he had come so far by himself. There were many discussions about me, but always in Yiddish. I knew they were talking about me. I attended Friday evening and Saturday services and was the centre of attention. On Sunday, my father arrived.

No life is a straight line. There are peaks and valleys that we climb over or travel through and each crossroad leads to another crossroad. That day was another crossroad for me. Another invisible notch that cut into my soul and altered my life. Should not a child love their parents? Is not love the chain that holds a family together? Why then did my father not love me? Or, if he did, why did he never show it? Years later, a lifetime later, I stood before his grave in Israel and faced the stone that identified him from the many around him. Here he lay, a cache of painful memories, and I, now as old if not older than he was when he arrived by taxi to bring me home, can only remember the event as another link in a chain that I would sever.

He came by taxi, a journey of one hundred kilometres, that must have cost him a fortune. A fortune he never had. I suspect that he spent many years paying back whoever lent him the money to make this journey. He was a proud man who never asked of others. How this must have hurt his pride! As each kilometre passed, the anger must have built.

When I saw him, I was frightened beyond belief. At any moment I expected to be beaten with his strap, to be yelled at for what I had done, but miraculously that never happened. We returned to Cluj-Napoca that same day in the taxi. I sat as far from him as was possible, neither of us spoke, and I expected that when we reached home, I would be punished.

But it wasn't the kind I expected.

My mother and sisters tearfully hugged and kissed me when we arrived. My father left me with them. The evening meal was placed on the table and I took my place. Before I had a chance to eat, my father grabbed my hand and took me out to the woodshed. I expected him to remove his strap, but instead he took a long heavy rope, tied it around my foot and attached it to the woodshed, then pushed me to the ground. In all this time, he had never said a word. Not during the miles we travelled, not from the time we arrived and not at the dinner table. I lay there and looked up at him as he towered over me. "If you act like a roaming dog, you can live like one," he said and left me.

The evening darkness covered me. Instead of fear, I was elated that he had not used his belt. I continued to lie there. Only one leg was restricted. I could have removed the rope, but to do that would have meant flouting my father's authority. The rope was long enough that if I wanted to crawl into the shed I could. Then hunger made itself felt. Hunger, darkness and the silence were my only companions. Loneliness can be as threatening as a weapon. A few hours passed and the hunger subsided. Much later, my mother brought me food. She waited while I ate and took everything back with her. Sleep finally came and, with it, the next day and another surprise.

It was noon. The main meal was on the verandah. I was still tied to the woodshed with my plate of food just outside. The cowbell over the front gate jangled and the elderly couple that had picked me up on the road entered. From where I sat outside the shed, I recognized them. I quickly took my plate of food and retreated inside. During the time I was with my father, he never asked and I never volunteered how I got from our home to his parents. Now the truth would be told, and if punishment loomed before, the thought of it overwhelmed me now, knowing that my father's temper would make me regret my actions. And I did regret what I had done.

Apparently, when I did not return home at the normal time, my mother sent my sisters to search for me. When they returned they told her that there was no school that day. My parents became frantic. The police were alerted, search parties sent out, rivers dragged, gypsy caravans searched and even a fortune teller consulted. Oddly enough, the fortune teller said that I was alive and well, with two old people in a valley between two high mountains. But still the search continued. Gypsies were known to steal children, cripple them and make them beg on the street. Those days I was missing were shear terror for my family. My action was impulsive, reckless and not thought through. And at this time, irreversible.

I heard laughter. The couple had read in the newspaper about what I had done and had come to see if it was the same boy that they had befriended. They were telling my parents and sisters what I had said to them. More laughter. My sisters ran from the verandah to the woodshed and excitedly told me our father wanted me to come to the verandah. I untied the rope and made my way to where he sat.

My father asked me if what he was told was true. I admitted it was. He told me I had to apologize to the couple for lying.

I did.

He ordered me to write five hundred times, "I will never tell a lie, and I will never run away again."

So I did.

My punishment was over. Life could now return to normal. In time, I would not only break one of the promises, I would break them both. That year was 1939.

THE DIFFICULT YEARS

TWO WEEKS AFTER my birthday, March 23, 1939, the German and Romanian governments signed an agreement that guaranteed the predominance of Germany in the Romanian economy. Romania had oil. Lots of oil. Oil that would become an important commodity to the Germans in a few short months. Germany also had the Nuremberg Laws. In time, Germany would export hate and import our oil.

When the Second World War broke out, Romania was under Carol II's dictatorial government. In 1938, threatened by the rise to power of the Nazi-like Iron Guard, which he himself had earlier encouraged, Carol dissolved all parties and concentrated power in his own hands. His domestic policies were aimed at holding in check the expanding power of the Iron Guard and, in foreign affairs, he tried to keep Romania neutral between the Allies and the Axis, though leaning closer to the Axis.

Anti-Semitic organizations had long been active in Romania. During the 1930s, these organizations established close ties with the National Socialists in Germany and the Foreign Policy Department of the Nazi Party. The economic depression of the early 1930s had a particularly devastating effect on agriculture, which was the source of livelihood of 78 percent of the population. It wasn't much of a leap for a farmer to hate Jews. Jewish bankers extended credit and Jewish merchants served as middlemen in the distribution of their produce, locally and abroad. When their credit turned into debts that could not be repaid, they lost their properties. The Jews were blamed.

Karl Adolf Eichmann would implement the Final Solution in 1942. The Jews gave the people an enemy to focus on, someone to blame for all their problems. So get rid of the problem by getting rid of the Jews. Say it enough times and it is believed. Do it under the guise of law and it becomes legal. The unacceptable becomes acceptable.

The collapse of Poland and then of France led Carol II to sever his Anglo-French ties on July 1, 1940 and to proclaim Romania a "neutral ally" of the Axis. Three days earlier, the Soviet Union, having occupied half of prewar Poland, demanded the cessation of northern Bucovina and all of Bessarabia to which, on Germany's advice, Carol II promptly ceded. Shortly after, Romania gave up the northern part of Transylvania to Hungary. A week later, Romania ceded southern Dobruja to Bulgaria. Gradually, Romania was being carved up into pieces. Whatever aspirations Carol II had were of no consequence. His country was a country in name only.

BY THE TIME I was eleven in 1941, we had moved three more times, each time to a bigger home. The last time to a three-apartment complex, one storey high, with a cold cellar, a vegetable garden, a pigsty, a barn, chicken coop, three storage sheds and, most important, a two-seat outhouse with a head-high partition. Nearby was a community well with a hand pump. In our eyes, this was luxury. We lived in the third apartment, consisting of one large kitchen and one large bedroom. The kitchen became my father's tailor shop and, with the permission of the landlord, my father hung a sign on the front gate that advertised his services: Moricz Jozsef, paraszt szabo, which meant a tailor specializing in traditional clothing. We had moved into an enclave of a sect of Hungarian peasants.

With the annexation of Transylvania by Hungary as a reward for becoming Germany's ally, we were no longer considered Romanians, but Hungarians. This pleased my father, as he was pro-Hungarian. At one time before and during the First World War, Transylvania was part of the Austro-Hungarian Empire. During that war, my father served in the Austro-Hungarian army and learned German. The fact that my father fought alongside Germany and spoke German would be instrumental in saving my life later.

No longer in a Jewish environment and no longer required to attend Jewish parochial school, I was permitted to grow my hair once again, cut off my side locks and not wear a yarmulke. I again became one of them.

When Hungary became Germany's ally, the army requisitioned one of the apartments for two cavalry soldiers billeted in Cluj-Napoca and took over the barn for their horses. This was my first contact with the war. I was too young to understand what was happening.

What is war? As a child, it is a game in which friends hide and make believe they are shooting at each other. A time when they kill or are killed, then laugh and play some more. It is a game until the game takes a real life. I have tried to recall what I could in remembering my first recollections of the war and I find that it wasn't a part of my life. That is, until later, years later, when I was not an observer but a participant. Then death, real death, touched me and war was no longer a game.

As an adult I learned things I never knew as a child. Europe was a continent isolated by invisible boundaries, protected by walls of ignorance and fed the words of lies to prevent the truth from being told. The dying was taking place only kilometres from our borders and the adults heard what they were told, believed what they wanted and lived their lives as if they would be untouched by the war, untouched by death. Stories filtered past the walls, carried by word of mouth, exaggerated or minimized depending on the teller. The war was growing like a brush fire. Its appetite was for the innocent. Its brain was Adolf Hitler.

Like a wave, the dates of infamy had begun to build. January 1937, Hitler denounced the treaty of Versailles, claiming Germany had rights. March 1938, German troops marched into Austria to quell the so-called public disorder. October 1938, Hitler marched into Czechoslovakia's Sudetenland. November 1938, Kristallnacht. Jewish property in Germany and Austria was destroyed or confiscated. January 1939, Hitler demanded the Port of Danzig from Poland and promised that if war came, he would annihilate the Jewish race in Europe. March 1939, Hitler took all of Czechoslovakia. September 1, 1939, at 4:45 a.m., Germany invaded Poland. April 1940, Hitler gave the order to invade Norway and Denmark. May 1940, Holland, Belgium and Luxemburg fell. June 1940, France became the next casualty. The countries of Europe fell like dominos, as the juggernaut rolled over them, consolidating what it had conquered, resting before turning its eyes eastward. And all the while, we in Romania or

Hungary or whatever they called it, remained oblivious to the death and pain. The bubble we lived in remained intact.

For the next three years, I went to school and worked for a company that did home renovations. I mixed plaster, wove reeds, mixed concrete for sidewalks and foundations and mixed mortar for brick laying. On March 9, 1943, at the age of thirteen, I had my Bar Mitzvah and, in the eyes of God and Jews, became an adult. As Orthodox Jews, we observed the Sabbath.

It was not a day of work and many tasks that we today take for granted were forbidden by the Torah, and as such we depended on a Shabbas goy, a Sabbath gentile, to do that which we were not permitted to do. He would turn off the lights late Friday evening, light the fire in the stove on Saturday mornings, fetch our noon meal from the baker and do any other chores, however menial, that could be interpreted as work. So, what was a Jew? Someone not gentile. It wasn't until September 1943 that I realized what being Jewish meant. I also learned what an Aryan was.

I had just started grade seven in September 1943 when the ordinance came out requiring all Jews to wear a yellow Star of David sewn onto the upper front left side of their clothing. Those born of mixed marriages had to wear a white Star of David. Now the nickname "*kicsi zsido*", little Jew, took on a new meaning, a derogatory meaning, a designation of contempt fuelled by the hatred of adults and then passed on to their children. Now Jews could not hide their religion by integrating. They were obvious by the Star of David prominently displayed on their clothing and the good gentiles hurled verbal abuse on us as we went about our restricted lives. My father was even struck. Often I was accosted by several children and hit and punched. My gentile friends became my gentile tormentors, all, except Egon, our Sabbath Goy. He, and he only, remained a friend and stopped many more beatings that were waiting for me.

My father's business sign was vandalized and he was ordered to remove it. The grocer, who was not Jewish, was ordered to no longer give us credit. My father's gentile clients dwindled. Money became scarce. Fear was in abundance. We had no idea how we would survive. The weeks passed, the anger against Jews mounted and the future appeared bleak. Then we received the order that we were to be deported to a labour camp.

At thirteen, my perception of events was not at all how my perception would have been now. I had young eyes that saw only what amused or interested me. No matter what was happening beyond my knowledge, it was not something that I retained as fear. For me to be afraid, events had to be personal. They weren't. My friends had always taunted me, so what was different about that? I had to wear a Star of David. It was not a symbol of shame to me, but of fact. I was a Jew. My movements weren't restricted. Where could I go, anyway? I had tried to run away once and I wasn't interested in trying it again. At least not yet. So my father had to take down his sign. What does that mean to a thirteen-year-old? That we didn't have credit in the grocery store was something of which I was not aware. I was never hungry. Maybe my parents were. At what point does reality set in?

At the end of February 1944, my employer's son, a police captain, came to our apartment. He spoke to my parents for a few minutes and my mother began to cry. My father ordered my sisters and me to the bedroom. We tried to hear what was being said but they whispered. We heard the front door close and my mother's tears turned to hysteria.

Fear!

That was the first moment of reality.

We cowered in the room, fearing we knew not what, hearing my mother's cries and incoherent mumblings. Never had my mother appeared to us in such a state.

The fear swept over my sisters and me and we cried, not knowing why we cried.

My father finally calmed my mother, for she gradually started sobbing again. My father's voice penetrated the door as he told us to come out. Subdued, staring at our mother as her muffled sobs squeezed from between the fingers that buried her face, we edged into the kitchen. My father had the look of a person who was forcing himself to face a terrible decision. His eyes seemed glazed as he looked not at us but about the room. We stood before him, waiting for him to speak. Finally he said, "We are to leave here and go to a labour camp. We have three days. We take only what we can carry."

The Aktsia, which had started in 1942 throughout occupied Europe, had finally come to us. Our bubble had burst.

Just three small sentences, but they would change our lives forever. A lifetime of accumulation was to be left behind, stolen from us because . . . we were Jews.

No one else was going to labour camps – only Jews.

No one else had to wear a yellow star on their coats – only Jews.

No one else had a curfew – only Jews.

Who feared whom?

DURING THE NEXT two nights, there were visits from our neighbours. All the windows were darkened due to air-raid regulations. When a gentile neighbour knocked, we would turn off the lights before opening the door. In whispers, they talked and asked questions of what would happen to us. No one knew. Speculation was rampant. Theories were many. But no one knew what to expect. By the time the day of the evacuation arrived, many items were missing from our kitchen and bedroom. What little we received in compensation was as much as those who paid could afford.

At 10:00 a.m., my family stood on the street with whatever we could carry, waiting for the transportation to take us away. My mother was in tears. The neighbours stood on both sides of the street to watch. It was cold. It was not the type of weather for standing about doing nothing. Time ticked away – our transportation was late. Some of the neighbours talked to us, offering words of encouragement. Egon, the boy who always protected me, came to say goodbye. Time ticked ever so slowly in the cold. It was not until 11:00 a.m. that a flatbed, single horse-drawn freight cart arrived to pick us up. By then, the neighbours were gone, for it had become too cold for them to stand outside and wait.

There were two families already in the wagon and two more were picked up before we arrived at the old brickyards. Many thousands of Jews were brought to this place where bricks had once been made and the brickyards became a community within a community. It became our ghetto. We were searched as we passed through the gate. Radios and newspapers were confiscated. The outside world no longer existed. We lived in rubble. Hungarian soldiers patrolled the fence that imprisoned us. There was no Judenrat to speak on our behalf. As our numbers swelled, sanitary conditions diminished. When the building could hold no more occupants, the outside grounds became home for those still arriving. Life was harsh. My mother cried often, frequently embracing my sisters and me, and prayed. If God heard, he must have been preoccupied. No amount of prayer changed our predicament. Throughout this terrible ordeal, my father appeared detached and uncaring. Never in that time did he comfort my mother. Never did he show his children any physical affection. This man who had insisted on sending his only son to a parochial school didn't even pray.

About three weeks passed before they began assembling people into groups, then marching us to the railway yards to be taken, we were told, to a labour camp. Our turn came in March. As I think back, I hadn't realized the significance of the month of March. I was born in March. Romania signed her life away to Germany in March. Germany took Austria in March. My Bar Mitzvah was in March. Czechoslovakia fell in March. And in March 1944, we were on our way to the labour camp. By this time Cluj-Napoca was judenrein. No one knew what a labour camp was or what was expected of us. It would take three days before we would have all the answers, for the labour camp was no labour camp, it was Auschwitz-Birkenau, the largest extermination camp in Europe. Our only function there was to die immediately upon arrival.

LIVING THROUGH THE HOLOCAUST

AT THE RAILWAY station, a long train of cattle cars awaited us. We sat with our legs spread, so the next person could sit between our legs, jammed like sardines until the only space not taken by human flesh were the four corners of the car, where empty pails were placed to be used as toilets. We were about one hundred to a car, ranging from suckling babies to the very old. Many times I had to plug my ears with my fingers to get a respite from the terrible din of crying babies, arguments, shouting, praying and fighting. We travelled through the night. By the next day the stench became unbearable, especially for those closest to the corners. Several times we stopped, but were never fed or the pails replaced. On the second day, at about noon, the train once again came to a stop. The doors on both sides were opened and two men from each side were ordered to remove the pails of human waste and dump them. From each side of the car, a pail of drinking water and a tin cup was circulated. The Hungarian soldiers were silent. They had been ordered to say nothing. Questions and pleading from the people in the cars fell on deaf ears.

The ordeal had taken its toll on body and spirit. Physically ill, weak, hungry and demoralized, their dignity shattered, humiliated by having to do their toilet in public, people gulped the water as if it were the essence of life – for in fact it was, briefly. When they finished, the Hungarian guards withdrew, to be replaced by the German Wermacht, the regular soldiers. Later, I learned that the exchange had taken place at the Polish border. The train continued on its journey.

Rumours fueled arguments as the train sped closer to its destination. Labour camps would be better than what was happening to them on the train. Some said we were on our way to Madagascar, an island where all the Jews were going to live. Everyone had an opinion. Rumours of hope. Words to believe in. We had experienced abuse, hunger and cold. We had been uprooted. I watched my mother's despair and my father's indifference to her plight and I still believed all would be well. We all believed it would be well.

The train came to a jolting halt.

We had arrived at our destination.

The word *toit* was whispered. It was time to die.

Hans Frank, governor of southern Poland, was responsible for the deportation and massacre of more than 2.5 million Jews from the ghettos and death camps. Heinrich Himmler's decree was now to be implemented. Only one door was opened. At each end were men in striped clothing with a row of numbers sewn onto the breast pocket and a yellow triangle above the numbers. All along the length of the train were soldiers in black uniforms, the *hakenkreux* badge on their arms, German shepherd dogs on leashes at their sides. There were shouts from *shutzstaffeln* as they screamed their orders, "Raus! Raus! Schnell! Schell! Out! Out! Quick! Quick!" We stumbled from the cars, cramped, weak, unable to stand, our legs stiff from lack of use. We were forced into groups and made to stand in front of our car. Terrified by the noise, the dogs and the menacing soldiers, people became unnerved and cried, screamed and even prayed to a God who had become deaf to their plight. Soldiers placed themselves in front of us, their faces grim, their dogs lunging on their leashes.

The two men in the striped clothes mingled with the prisoners and tugged at the women to form another group. My mother refused to release my hand, but they pulled at her until they broke her grip. Screaming, she was dragged away with my sisters. Moans of grief tore through the air as the men called after their wives, their daughters and friends. My father watched, silent, detached, observing but aloof. The wails continued until the women were out of sight. By nightfall, most would be dead, their remains the black soot that puffed into the sky, their grave.

A member of the SS would climb onto the roof of the gas chamber. The people would enter, naked, wailing as the door closed behind them. Ten minutes would pass and then there was silence. When the door opened, the bodies would be stacked like a pyramid as the strong climbed over the bodies of the weak trying to reach the ceiling in hopes the gas would not float that high. But all was in vain. The bodies were dragged from the room by Jews and loaded onto wagons to be taken to a ditch until they could be brought to the incinerators. My mother was among them. To this day I don't know if my father ever said prayers for her. Even under his breath.

The men were marched to the men's camp, separated into smaller groups in front of a large building, stripped naked and made to stand outside in the cold. To keep warm, we jumped up and down, clasping our arms across our bare chests, hugging whatever warmth we could generate. The door to the building eventually opened and we were ordered inside. It was a large shower room. We must have been two hundred in number. The door closed behind us and, for a brief moment, we were unsure what was going to happen. The room was sterile in appearance, only water nozzles protruded from the ceilings, and the hollowness of our combined voices echoed off the ceiling. We did not have long to wait. From another door a small column of prisoners in striped clothing emerged, carrying hair clippers and razors. The men had all their body hair removed, head, chest, arms, legs and around the genitals. I had only my head shaved. Our individuality was removed. We were identical. Sizes and shapes varied, but, physically, we looked alike. We showered, were sprayed with disinfectant powder and handed clothes, some new, some not. We were called *untermensch*.

One beret-type striped cap

One striped jacket (no shirt)

One pair of pants (no underwear)

One striped below-knee-length overcoat

One pair of boots with eyelets and hooks for laces. The boots were made of some kind of plastic material and the thick soles were made of wood.

One metal soup bowl and spoon. Each had wire hooks so they could be hooked onto our rope-belt.

Achtung! Achtung! We were lined up in columns on the appel platz. A detail of prisoners brought out huge cauldrons of steaming liquid. Having not eaten in two days, my only thoughts, and those of all the men, were that we would finally be fed. What it was we didn't know. Kosher we knew it couldn't be. To eat unpurified food was forbidden by the Torah. To starve to death was forbidden by the Torah. We had lost everything but our religion. Now it seemed we were to be stripped of that, too.

Would God understand?

Did He care?

The soup smelled delicious. A line formed and I edged closer to the cauldrons, my bowl ready in my hand. Prisoners whose faces were masks of anonymity, unsmiling, wooden and impersonal, poured the liquid into my bowl, robots programmed to perform a task. I tasted the liquid and found it foul. Hunger prevented me from spitting it out. Every drop was forced into my mouth and when I finished, I licked my plate.

SS officers entered the parade grounds and ordered us into rows of six. Using his swagger stick, one officer slowly strolled along the rows, scrutinizing us like inspecting cattle. His stick would point towards a prisoner and indicate whether he should move to the right or to the left of the row. When he finished, those on the right appeared healthier and stronger than those on the left. Later, I was to learn that left meant death.

I was on the left.

I looked at my father and I couldn't believe what I saw.

There were tears on his cheek. Were they for me?

The soldiers marched the men on the right away. Those on the left were again separated, this time into three columns: The old, infirm, crippled and weak on the left, the children in the middle and whoever was deemed salvageable on the right. I was among these.

The boys were marched away to what was referred to as the men's section, the third barrack from the end. The men's section was about half a kilometre long and two hundred meters wide and surrounded by electric wire and watchtowers. The building housed between three and four hundred boys, age five and up. In fact, the last three building housed boys only. Four or five boys were assigned to each bunk bed, which were three tiers high, with no mattresses and no bedding, only boards. When the guards left and the building darkened, the younger boys cried and called for their mothers. The older boys tried to comfort them, but to no avail. Darkness is a mixed blessing. To some, it represents the unknown and allows terrible images to prey on the mind. To others it hides the truth, the ugliness of reality. But it cannot hide sounds and smells. It cannot prevent loneliness, even in the presence of four hundred boys. It cannot make the bad go away.

The next morning, we were marched out of the barrack and permitted to use the latrine, then lined up on the parade grounds and given a bowl of food. For hours we stood in the cold, waiting for what – we knew not. We saw the children from the very last barrack being marched out through the gate. The cold penetrated my thin garments and, no matter whether I wrapped my arms across my chest or flapped them, I couldn't stop shivering. Never could I remember being so cold, and for so long.

Finally we were allowed to return to our barrack. There was no more food, no more water given us. A pail was again our toilet. We bundled together on our bunks to keep warm and wished the long day to end. At last darkness settled on us, our second night. The lucky ones slept. The heat from the bodies on both sides of me gave me some warmth, my arms were my pillows, my eyes were closed, but my mind would not let me sleep. I heard the door open and lifted my head. Several men had come into the building. Names were being called. I heard mine. I left the bunk and recognized my father. He took my hand and told me to be silent. In small groups, the men and their sons left the barrack and silently made their way to the men's barrack. It was then we were told that all the children were being sent to the gas chambers. The children we had seen leave earlier in the day were dead.

The next day the guards noticed us but said nothing. They fed us once a day. Four days went by. On the fifth, after being fed, we were formed into columns and marched from the compound to a large parade ground next to the railway line where other prisoners were already waiting. Most were men. Very few were children. Again we were separated, but not by age or height. An officer walked before each prisoner and poked a stick into his chest. If they fell back, they went to the left.

I fell back.

My father watched without expression. To my surprise he broke rank, which was forbidden, and approached the highest-ranking officer and spoke to him in German. What did he say? Did he tell him he fought with Germany? Did he beg for my life? I never found out. All I know was that the officer indicated I join my father. The others on the left were taken away.

We were leaving Auschwitz-Birkenau. I had *mazel*. To stay would have meant meeting Dr. Josef Mengele. To meet the doctor, famous for his experiments on children, was a death sentence. We boarded the train, packed like sardines. The ride lasted two days with one meal each day and six pit stops. Those unable to last to a pit stop soiled themselves and often the one beside them. The car was relatively quiet. We knew that for the moment we were needed someplace. Death was not at the immediate end of the trip, though we sensed it was not too far away.

We arrived in Mauthausen in Austria. We had come far. From Hungary to Poland and now to Austria, and always there were Germans. Would the quarries of Mauthausen be any different from the extermination camp of Auschwitz-Birkenau? It wouldn't take long to find out. On the train was my godfather, a middle-aged man, normally quiet and easy to get along with. A soldier struck him with his rifle butt as he got off the train. He went berserk and attacked the soldier. Several other soldiers rushed over and stabbed my godfather to death with their bayonets. Was Mauthausen to be any different? Only the guards.

In 1937, by order of Adolf Hitler, Mauthausen concentration camp had been built beside a quarry. Hitler had appointed Albert Speer to design the grounds for the exploitation of slave labour for German Earth and Stone Works Corporation, an SS-run corporation under the direction of Heinrich Himmler. It turned out to be a very successful enterprise. In January 1941, the camp's designation was changed from a slave labour camp to a Category III camp, an annihilation camp. Those deemed beyond rehabilitation, enemies of the country, were sent to Mauthausen at the beginning and later, as the war progressed, everyone was sent. Compared to other Category III camps, Mauthausen had a death rate of 58 percent as compared to 36 percent in Dachau, 19 percent at Buchenwald and 16 percent in Sachsenhausen. The question of how many people died in Auschwitz-Birkenau, the largest death camp has been shrouded in mystery. Early estimates were based on assumptions, but recent numbers have established that 1.1 million inmates were killed, most of them Jews.

The weak were loaded into big vans, the rest were marched to the main camp, stripped, showered and disinfected. We were given *klamotten*, striped prison clothing, and were fed. Afterwards, we were marched to an empty barrack and assigned bunks. The bunks were wide and four-tiered, running the length of the barrack, with three to four metre aisles between rows. A Block Eltester was put in charge of the barrack. The soldiers withdrew and we were free to go to the latrines whenever we wanted and free to walk within the camp enclosure.

Free, of course, is a relative term. Although we were allowed more freedom in this place than we had had in Auschwitz-Berkenau, we were still imprisoned, still without rights, and could die at the whim of anyone of authority.

The next day we were given five-or-six digit numbers on strips of cloth and a coloured triangle designating our religion and had them sewn onto our uniforms. The fact that we were numbered and classified initially gave us the assurance we would live – at least for the moment. We learned that those taken away in the vans were dead before they reached the crematoriums. The vans were portable death vehicles equipped with vents that released gas to kill those in the back within minutes.

For four days we did nothing but wait and wonder, watching others being selected and taken from the barrack. Others who never returned. On the fifth day, about fifty of us were marched from the barrack by a *kommandfuher* to the rail tracks and put onto a short train. It travelled for about an hour. Our destination was a large military base and concentration camp near the city of Melk, the home of a large Benedictine abbey and the location of Shallaburg castle, both tourist attractions today. We were searched, counted and separated into small groups, then taken to Block 11. The inmate in charge of our Block, or barrack, was called a kapo. A kapo in most cases was a German criminal released from jail and transferred to a concentration camp to be the willing servant of the SS. Later, some were Jews. He wore the same uniform as we did. He also wore a solid beret with a green triangle over his number – a badge of dishonour.

My father and I were still together in the same barrack. The camp was huge. There were rows upon rows of barracks as far as the eye could see, holding about 20,000 prisoners, I would later learn. A crematorium, a hospital, which no one wanted to go to, and a huge kitchen complex were the main buildings. The best job to have in any of the camps was in the kitchen and the only ways to get it were through bribery or connections. For every six barracks, there was a central latrine and shower. For every barrack, there were two hundred inmates. For every two hundred inmates, there was one kapo, one man playing the role of God. A man to be feared even over the Nazis for he watched, he judged, he hated and he condemned. He had a room to himself at the end of the barrack, his own stove and a large window through which he could monitor our activities. He also had the responsibility of work assignments.

My first assignment was the next day. Six guards escorted thirty of us from the camp, past the military base to where additional barracks were being built and I was assigned as a helper to a civilian Austrian carpenter. I could not understand anything he said. He lost his temper so many times when I didn't understand his orders that I feared I would be taken away, but whenever the soldiers asked him if he still wanted the little guy for his helper, he always nodded. After one week,

I learned some German expressions and, from gestures and my past experiences from my construction job, I was able to guess what tools and materials he needed. By the third week, he was teaching me the language and sharing the food from his lunch box.

One morning my father woke me early and told me that I was being transferred to his work detail. I cried and begged to be allowed to stay with the carpenter, but to no avail. My father had made a made-to-measure suit for the kapo and convinced him to have me transferred. Although he never said why, he wanted me transferred. I knew he was concerned for my safety. As it turned out, my size and weight would work against me. His work detail was hard and exhausting. At 4:00 a.m. we would line up for *appel* (roll call), then board a train for the one-hour ride to our location, a mountain where we dug a myriad of tunnels in order to construct a ball-bearing factory within.

As our train arrived, the previous shift left. Three shifts a day, seven days a week, the human diggers came and left. From one of the rail cars, big steaming cauldrons of strong black coffee were unloaded. We were given one full ladle of it and one lump of sugar. Those who saved some of the bread from the previous meal had something to eat. Those who did not, watched with envy and hunger. The work was backbreaking. After unloading a train, we had to immediately shovel the concrete up the scaffolding and be ready for the next train. There was no rest until the shift was over, and then you were either exhausted or dead. The wall of the tunnel was lined with multilevel scaffolds. The higher the scaffold assignment, the less physical the work. I was assigned to the top level. The men shoveled the concrete up to the next level, where a crew shoveled it to the next and another crew to the next until it reached my level. Our job was to shovel the concrete into the forms that became the new walls of the tunnel; inside the forms were prisoners who, using one-and-a-half-metre sticks, poked the stick up and down into the mass of concrete to rid it of air pockets. A month later I became a "switcher," a coveted job. I had to latch and unlatch the hopper cars and move the concrete around with a shovel to ensure that the cars were fully loaded. The work was significantly easier than the digging.

Cigarettes became the currency of the camp. With cigarettes, it was possible to get more food or privileges. My father, a heavy smoker before the war, now used them for barter. Fortunately for me, the civilian engineer I worked with often gave me extras, besides sharing his food with me. He was a *mensch*. Between my father and me, we were able to hoard fifteen cigarettes a week to better our lives. Each day the routine was the same. Each day was another day we survived. I took to recording my thoughts and my activities on paper, which along with my stub of a pencil, I kept in a secret pocket I had sewn into my jacket.

Our shift was usually over by mid-afternoon, at which point we were returned to the compound and counted. Periodically, we were searched for anything we might have appropriated from the workplace. One day when the soldier ran his hands over me, he felt the pencil and removed it and my one-page diary. It was written in Hungarian, so he did not know what it said. He demanded I tell him, but before I could do so, my father stepped forward and told him that he was my father and I just wrote some childish things. The soldier pocketed the items and never returned them.

At the end of our shift, we were able to move about the camp without restrictions. Also by this time, the "hairless" rule was no longer in effect and many had let their hair grow back and even had moustaches. With nothing to do, language classes sprang up and I took part in some. I now was able to speak in eight languages, though Yiddish became the most popular one. The evening meal was our most important meal; we were usually given a different soup from what we had at noon – if we were lucky, we would find a piece of meat in it – as well as one kilogram of black dense bread, and occasionally some butter and jam.

My father's ability as a tailor put him in good stead with many of the officers. He was making a uniform, as well as civilian clothes, for a high-ranking officer and for his labour he received extra rations which he shared with me. Death was a never-ending visitor to the camp, but we were able to hold him at bay. I was worried, however, about what I had written in my confiscated diary. In the wrong hands, the words were a death sentence.

Not long after the diary was taken, the kapo approached my father and whispered in his ear, then went to others and did the same. My father told me that we had to go to the parade ground. The *Lagerkommandant* had ordered that all father-and-son inmates were to attend a special *appel*. I was surprised to see about forty fathers with their sons in the line. One by one each set was ordered to step to the front where a soldier looked at them and then waved them away. When my father and I stepped forward, he looked at me and yelled, "This is the one!" Only then did it dawn on me that the soldier was the one who had confiscated my diary. All the others were dismissed, leaving my father and me alone before the soldier and the high-ranking officer. My legs were shaking with fear. My father stared at me, having no idea of the seriousness of what I had done, since he had never read my scribblings. The thoughts I'd recorded revealed my hatred for the Germans. The most demanding statement was "too bad more of the SS didn't die in that air raid." I was referring to a recent air raid in which the Allied planes dropped bombs in the vicinity and killed 2,000 prisoners but only a handful of Nazis. It seemed a high price for so few who were meant to die.

The punishment for serious disciplinary infractions was hanging. The victim was hanged in the parade grounds and left for two or three days as a reminder to the others of what could be expected if they disobeyed orders. Only the week before, two were hanged for trying to escape. I wasn't trying to escape. Was what I had done considered serious?

The officer beckoned my father to step forward. He did so and was handed the diary. As he read, his face turned ashen. He pleaded in German with the officer. I watched, unable to understand the words but I recognized from the look on my father's face and the gestures of his hands that he was pleading for my life. The officer stood rigid as a pole, his face expressionless. My eyes darted to my father, to the officer, and back again. What was to be my fate? The officer eyed me with contempt. My father was still pleading my case when the officer issued his orders. The soldier marched us off the parade ground and into a building that housed the maintenance equipment. There I was ordered to drop my pants and touch my toes with my hands.

And then I understood.

I was to be lashed.

My father was asked to count the strokes. The soldier stepped forward with a whip and administered twenty-five lashes to my bare bottom. I screamed with pain for the first five or six lashes. After that I could not feel anything; my skin was numb. The whipping over, we were ordered back to our barrack. My father told me he knew the officer and had begged for a sentence other than death. My father had made him a suit of clothes that he was pleased with and was swayed by my father's plea. My life had been spared because of a made-to-measure suit. In hindsight, my life meant no more than a thank-you for a job well done.

When we got back to the barrack, everyone crowded around us, wanting to know what had happened. I was in pain, my skin was broken and blood ran in rivulets down my legs. I could not sit. I walked until the lights were turned off, then lay in my bunk on my stomach. Tears flowed then. Tears of pain and of anger and hate. I became filled with resolve. I would live. I would never forget this day. I never have.

Because I was forced to sit, the train ride the next day was a journey of pain. The workday brought on more pain and the journey back to the compound was an endless stream of pain. It was three weeks before I could sit without pain.

As the weeks passed, my father's and my fortune improved. A new civilian engineer took over our section, an Austro-Hungarian. He and my father struck up a relationship. My father's cigarette allotment increased and he was promoted to the top of the scaffold. The Allied bombers flew by on a daily basis. Bombs fell but none hit the tunnel where we were working. More time passed and the planes stopped coming. What did come was the winter of 1944-1945 and with it, changes.

I crushed my right thumb while switching cars. I didn't want to go to the camp hospital, for to go was too often never to return. The new engineer, Janos, poured vodka on it, covered it with black axle grease and bandaged it with a rag. Again I suffered the pain in silence, not wanting the soldiers to know, fearing that if they did, they would think I was unable to work and then . . .

This was also a cold winter and our clothing proved quite inadequate. The kapos and some of the privileged prisoners were allowed to wear heavy civilian clothing. Some had hats with earflaps and many had pullovers and even knit gloves. As for the prisoners, they were given an overcoat but were forbidden to wear two. They could purchase, with cigarettes, any number of coats on the black market, because with so many dying from exhaustion, malnutrition and disease, their clothing became available. But no amount of cigarettes could purchase a second coat. Instead, padded linings were made to go inside a coat.

Now my father and I, and anybody with tailoring skills, were busy sewing these linings. My father sewed linings into our trousers, too, and made many of us gloves and socks. When sleeping, we doubled up, using body heat to keep warm. We had been promised winter blankets, but they never arrived. Our food rations decreased. Soup became almost all water. Our bread rations were cut in half. The war was going badly for the Germans and we were feeling the brunt of it. The black market flourished but, as the commodities became harder to obtain, the price of purchasing skyrocketed. Cigarettes were more than currency – they were life itself.

One cold morning when I arrived at my workstation, I found my ten-car hopper train parked on one of the rail branches near the chutes with no driver and the engine off. When the works manager arrived, he was very upset about being unable to deliver the concrete. I faced the cab while he ranted and raved up and down the length of the train. I don't know why I did what I did, but I chose that moment to step up to the cab and climb in. I suppose that *chutzpah* is the word that best describes my action. I opened the compressed gas tank and started the engine. The train putt-putted to life. When the works manager raced back to the cab and saw me inside, his face turned red with anger. He seemed about to explode. The engine continued to putt-putt and the realization of what I had done must have sunk in, because his expression changed, his face broke out in a wide grin and, as he jumped on the step of the cab, he said, "Good boy, let's go."

I started the train jerkily, edging closer to the maze of tracks that spider-webbed away from the station. Not knowing how to work the brakes properly, I overshot the first rail switch and had to back up. With the works manager as my switcher and many shocked onlookers, we rolled and jerked our way to the loading chutes. As each hopper was filled, I edged the next under the chute until the whole train was loaded and I could take the train to the tunnel. At the tunnel, the works manager told me, "Tell the kapo to give you a switcher." Everyone was in awe that I had been given permission to pick my own switcher. I picked my father.

Although I never found out what happened to the previous engineer and I had lost him as a source of extra food, the works manager increased my cigarette allotment to twenty cigarettes a week and, when he learned that my switcher was my father, he increased his to fifteen. Now my father was able to smoke the occasional cigarette. A few times a week I would find some bread left in the cab and occasionally a small piece of kolbasa. Although I never learned who left the food, I always suspected the works manager. He was a very kind person.

It was not long after I became an engineer that other prisoners were allowed to become engineers. It was harder to find civilians to do the job. It was harder to find anything. By mid-February, conditions in the camp worsened. The rations were cut further, even our cigarettes, but the lack of black market products declined also and my father took to smoking more. Even I started smoking.

On the third week of February, we assembled for work only to be told to return to our barracks. As it got light, we noticed the midnight shift was in the barracks as well. Later we were issued a two-metre length of rope and told to roll our blankets and make a knapsack, include our eating utensils, and to assemble on the parade grounds. There were 20,000 prisoners and several units of soldiers. We were evacuating the camp. The Russians were advancing. We were about to embark on a long trip. Many would never reach the end of the journey.

THE DEATH MARCH

THE LINE OF prisoners seemed endless. As far as I could see ahead and behind me, the straggling prisoners shuffled their way towards Linz, to Salzburg and then to Ebensee, with our numbers decreasing with each mile. History would record these treks as death marches. First the sick dropped out, shots were fired, always shots, one, sometimes two, to end the pain of someone who could no longer place one foot ahead of the other. Then the body was dragged off the road. No one even turned his head to see who had met his death. It was just another heap of bones and wasted flesh, sticking out from clothes whose owner no longer cared. When we passed one, we averted our eyes, focused on willing our exhausted and hungry bodies forward. Forward, but to where?

The trek never stopped except for brief pit stops every four hours and for the night. For ten long, painful days we marched and, for the first two, we were never fed. From Linz to Salzburg we were fed once. As we passed many villages, we encountered acts of kindness from several women. They would stand by the side of the road with baskets of food and, as the front of the column trudged by, they would throw the food – carrots, parsnips, cabbage and apples – to us. Sometimes even bread. Chaos ensued. Like animals, hungry men lunged for the food on the ground, some ignoring the fists that struck them as they tried to keep their grip on something that might sustain them another hour or another day. The soldiers ran to where the fighting occurred and shot into the thrashing bodies until order was restored. My father and I were in the middle of the column and unaffected by the frenzy, but in any event, there was too little food for too many.

My father and I had hidden in our blanket two large slabs of bread. Furtively we ate small portions and only during darkness, fearing that others would steal or forcibly take it from us. Water was not a problem. We were in the Tyrolean Alps and the countryside was covered in snow.

On the third day, we were taken to a soccer field and fed a hot thick vegetable soup. The soldiers complained about how little they were given. The next morning, after awakening from an extremely cold night, we discovered many of the prisoners had frozen to death and many others could no longer continue. By the time we reached Salzburg, about 10,000 dead prisoners marked our passage. And we still had miles to go.

We rested for two days, were fed once a day, mostly a watery soup, and took care of our own sick and dying. We noticed the soldiers were faring no better. On the seventh day of the march, we continued to our final destination which took us four more days. The surviving columns marched much more slowly and the fall-out was less. With each day, our march took us higher and higher into the Alps. The weather became milder and the soldiers less volatile in their response to the weary prisoners. As we passed through villages, the locals threw food to us and, this time, the soldiers were as anxious to catch it as we were.

As we neared Ebensee, the road became steeper, causing many to falter and drop. To my surprise, the soldiers ignored the fallen prisoners and double-marched us to the camp, being more anxious, we thought, to reach a place where they would be fed. We later learned they had run out of ammunition long ago and sent a detail back after they reached the camp to shoot the prisoners and cart them to the camp crematorium. Only a third of those who started reached the camp alive.

The camp became a jungle. We were assigned to a barrack, my father and I still together. The prisoners already in the barrack forcibly took the blankets from the new prisoners, too weak to resist. My father and I had lost ours on the trek. Our food ration was scarcely enough to keep us alive. To supplement what was given, we would peel the bark off the trees and mix it with water to fill our empty stomachs. Some resorted to cannibalism – there were corpses piled in front of the crematorium. To some, the unthinkable became acceptable.

Ebensee was no longer a work camp. It had been one of the forty-nine satellite camps of Mauthausen, a camp like Melk from where we had come, once an armament-production factory. Now it was a gathering of bodies. A place to wait and die. It was located high in the Tirrolean Alps in a picturesque area of forests, small lakes, ski slopes and hotels, a resort area used by the SS as a reward for exceptional deeds to the Fatherland.

Three weeks after we arrived, we were given our first work detail, the cleaning of a railway yard that had been bombed, about three hours march from the camp. Those selected were hardly able to stand, let alone walk. But to the 500 prisoners sent, it became an unexpected source of food. One of the destroyed buildings had been a machine shop. A common shaft driven by one motor powered almost all the equipment in the building. This shaft had a series of pulleys, spaced to line up with the machinery placed on the floor. Wide leather belts linking the machinery pulley to the common shaft-pulley drove the equipment. Because the belts were saturated with machine oil, during the fire these leather belts cooked in their own oil. We ate the belts.

Over the next two weeks, the death toll grew. Our barrack no longer was full. When the clean-up was finished, we were left in our barrack. Many were too weak to climb into a bunk and would lie on the floor. We hardly saw a soldier. About the second or third of May we noticed the watchtowers were no longer manned. The next day, there were no soldiers to be seen. Even the gateposts were abandoned.

One of the kapos, a German, known for his brutality, pleaded with the survivors not to turn him over to the advancing Allies. Three young Jewish boys attacked and killed him. Others would meet a similar fate before the camp was liberated.

On May 6, 1945, a reconnaissance patrol of three jeeps of American soldiers unexpectedly came upon our camp. Two of the jeeps entered the camp, the third returned to their unit to report. We numbered 25,000 to 30,000, most more dead than alive. Living skeletons. The living were gaunt, their heads shaven, sores on their bodies, some walked in a daze, some naked, others had blankets wrapped around them, their facial features normal, but everything else was completely out of proportion. Had the liberation occurred two weeks later, my father and I would not have survived. Thousands would not have survived.

I weighed only thirty kilos.

THE MIRACLE OF REUNION

OUR BARRACK WAS located at the far end of the camp, so it took some time for the news to reach us. We made our way to the front, in some cases even having to fight our way forward, hoping we would find food. We saw many truckloads of soldiers entering to restore order. When order was restored, army rations were delivered to each barrack. Those who were healthy and strong were given rides to the city. The weak and sick were to be given care. The army had no previous experience with how to treat starving prisoners and they fed us large quantities of rich food. Dysentery swept the camp and, before the diet could be corrected, thousands died. It was a tragic irony of our freedom that the victors, in trying to save the victims, killed those whom the Germans had not.

And there was retribution. Almost daily, the American army would round up some of the SS guards hiding in the forest. The most notable was the camp *Komandant* who was captured and put into the brig. When word reached the prisoners, several broke into the jail and dragged him to the middle of the camp where they tied him up and hanged him.

As the weeks passed, we slowly regained our strength. Our striped pyjamas were replaced with civilian clothes. It was then I saw something of my father that I had never seen before. Maybe this was the first of many threads that would tear apart our relationship. It is remarkable when I think about this incident, how small it was at the time and, yet, how significant it became. He cooked food for the men in our barrack. He actually cooked. Never to my knowledge had he cooked so much as an egg before the war.

Somehow he got hold of an army camp stove, some flour, oil, eggs and jam. To my amazement he made a large batch of *palacsinta* (very thin pancakes). Immediately the line began to form and the food was consumed as fast as he could dish it out. When he tired, I took over. I was shocked. Memories of my mother labouring almost twenty-four hours a day while he never helped overpowered me. Later, I did not see him as my saviour, not the man who had risked his life on many occasions for me, I saw only my mother. Why was this? Because she had died? I don't know. All I know is he cooked for strangers.

With the war over, I no longer feared death. Yes, I feared dying, but I didn't have to be afraid that I would be killed, or someone would abuse me, or any of a million reasons that I knew could end my life. There was now a new fear – living. I tried not to think about it. I survived. Many didn't. Did my mother? Did my sisters? Why me? For years I ate and slept with death and, although it was there, I learned to live with it. If I didn't, it would have swallowed me into its blackness and the will to live might have been sucked from me. As long as there is a will, there is hope. I willed myself to ignore what I saw, for not to would have jeopardized my existence. But now, there was no tension to help block out the thoughts, no fear to motivate my tired body to maintain its work schedule, no threats to me – and I now had free time to think. I lived, others died. Why? Such a small word and yet more than fifty years later I still ask myself the same question. Why? And I have no answer.

By the end of June 1945, we were told we could go home if we wished. My father and I applied to go home, were given I.D. papers, some money and train tickets. We took the train to Saltzburg and had to change when we entered the Soviet section. We travelled many days, passing Linz, Mauthausen and Vienna, then crossed into Hungary and, via Budapest, to the borders of Romania. We waited almost a day for a Romanian train to take us to Cluj, which was our final stop. It only took a few days to return from the death camp. It took a lifetime of memories to get there.

We stayed at a hostel for refugees. We asked other survivors if they had any news of my mother and sisters. They had none. We added our names to the posted names of survivors being accumulated by the International Red Cross and other agencies in hopes that if they had survived, they might see them and know we were alive. From the stories we heard, finding one another would be a miracle. My father went to our old flat to see if there was anything he could salvage. When he returned he told me that in a few days we would be moving back into our home. True enough, three days later we entered the premises and found almost all of our furniture still there. All that was missing were the two sewing machines and the last piece of furniture my father had bought – a divan on which my sister Lili had slept.

My father cooked our meals. I learned from him that he had been assigned to the kitchen during the Austro-Hungarian campaign and had been a cook. He knew how to cook many dishes. He didn't reveal this before because it wasn't considered manly to cook. That was a woman's chore. Since there were no women in our house, he cooked again.

My father knew I liked the metal trade and had me apprentice with a man he thought I would like. He was wrong. It was a dirty and monotonous job. After four weeks of coming home completely black from working with cast iron, I quit. My father was angry. The owner had done him a favour and my quitting had embarrassed him.

Not long afterwards, I placed myself into apprenticeship with a tool-and-metal die shop. After three months doing menial work, my training accelerated. One day during the lunch hour when all the machines were idle, I was told to try out a new die that I had just finished. This was the first die that my boss had let me build and I was very excited. My left hand was in the die, my foot on the pedal releasing the clutch of the press, and my right hand on the flywheel lowering the ram of the press. I was so engrossed in what I was doing that I was too slow to react to the squealing of the belts. One of the apprentices had started the motor not knowing I was working on one of the presses. I jerked my left hand out of the die instinctively, but not fast enough. The tip of my forefinger was sliced to the bare bone. I felt no pain. I was in shock. I yelled and my boss came running. He wrapped my finger in a cloth and took me, sitting on the crossbars of his bicycle, to the hospital. I had lost my left forefinger to the first joint. The next morning I returned to work.

This was also a time of reuniting. Over the next few months, people returned to their homes looking for family. My cousin Imre moved in with us. Imre had been ultra-orthodox before the war. He was being trained for a religious vocation; he had no trade. He apprenticed in truck driving. Imre travelled throughout Romania and on one such trip met my father's older brother, Arpad. When he returned home, he excitedly told us of his discovery. My father was indifferent. He had not seen or corresponded with his brother since the early 1930s and was not interested in his survival. I was. I journeyed to Brasov where my uncle and his family lived and spent four days with them. When I returned, my father's only comment was, "I guess I'll visit him one of these days." It took six more years before he did – and it was in Israel.

In mid-1945, my sister, Sari knocked on our door. My father, Imre and I were having dinner. A slight tapping on the wooden door caught our attention. I got up to answer and stood in shock as my sister stood before me, all smiles and tears. There was much hugging and kissing and crying, all the old enmity between us long forgotten. It was a miracle. Not only was Sari alive, but my sister Lili, she told us, had been liberated from Dachau concentration camp. Dachau was the first of the many infamous concentration camps that existed throughout Germany and Poland.

Sari told us what had happened to them after they'd been torn from my father and me in March 1944. When Sari, Lili and my mother arrived in Birkenau, the two girls were separated from my mother. The girls were then taken to Lager C and tattooed. Lili was assigned to the kitchen, while Sari was shipped after six weeks to a Gypsy camp, then back to Birkenau and then to Bergen-Belsen by forced march. It was during the march that a German guard shot Sari in the foot while she was trying to help a fallen prisoner. Sari weighed only thirty kilograms when liberated on May 15, 1945. Near the end of July, she found Lili's name listed as a survivor from Dachau and was making arrangements to go to her when Lili showed up. She'd seen Sari's name on a similar list.

After leaving Dachau, Lili went to Landsberg, Germany, a refugee camp, and worked as a nurse. At the camp she met Henry Cygelfarb, a uniformed camp policeman who was from Lodz, Poland, whom she later married. Sari and Lili returned to Landsberg and Sari stayed with Lili. Lili and Henry were married in April 1946. Before Sari returned to Cluj to find us, she met Albert Mimran, another Holocaust survivor, and they became engaged.

And our mother? After she was separated from my sisters, she was taken directly to the gas chambers. A simple statement of fact. At that time, my sisters had no idea what was happening. It was many days later when they learned about the chimney, the black smoke, the ovens.

THE RECOVERY YEARS

THE WAR HAD taken my mother and separated my sisters from my father and me. With the war over, the need to go on with life once again separated us. Lili and Henry made arrangements to go to France to live. Sari and Albert were going to Israel. Sari begged my father to come with her, but he refused. He was starting a new business, had a new life and didn't want to give up what he had started for another uncertain life. Besides, his roots were in Romania. It sounded convincing until later I was to learn he had another motive for staying. Women. Recently widowed women. One especially. One much younger than he. He claimed he was in love. Her name was Ilonka.

Sari stayed in Cluj and attended my father's wedding. My father and his new bride moved into her apartment and Father sold all our furniture and belongings and gave up our apartment. Ilonka didn't want any reminders of his previous marriage looking in her face and so Sari, Imre and I moved into a youth hostel. This was the first time I had been separated from my father since before the war, except for a few days in Auschwitz, and yet I was relieved. I wanted nothing to do with him. I resented Ilonka taking my mother's place, resented the way he fawned over his new bride, using words of endearment and an open display of affection. He had never treated my mother this way. My mother had toiled from early morning until late into the evening. He had never called her sweetheart or dear, never embraced her, never so much as placed an arm around her shoulders. It occurred to me as I watched him with his new wife that our home must have been an unhappy one and I felt my mother's pain. Scenes I had witnessed and never given any thought to took shape in my mind. I saw the sadness in my mother's face and realized what it meant.

A few weeks later, eight of us, including Sari and Imre along with a couple of friends, tried to cross into Hungary illegally. We were caught by Hungarian soldiers and returned to Romania. My father was unaware of our absence, oblivious to anything but his own life and Ilonkas. His world no longer included us. I wondered if it ever did. But then, if he didn't care about any of his children, why did he risk his life for me?

A couple of weeks later, a new group made the attempt without me and succeeded. From Hungary they made it to Austria, to a refugee camp in Vienna. Sari returned to Landsberg by train. Imre went to Italy, to a camp of young recruits for the Israeli underground army – the Hagganah. I was still in Cluj but, as circumstance would have it, not for long.

I returned to the tool-and-die shop. To my surprise, my father paid me a visit and invited me to Friday evening Sabbath meal. I accepted. As I watched Ilonka make the blessing over the candles, a great sadness came over me. The last time I had witnessed this ritual, it was my mother who blessed the candles. It set the mood for me for the rest of the evening. During the meal, my father turned to me and said, "Isn't this delicious?" In retrospect, innocent words, but it was as if acid had been poured on my heart. I answered, "My mother's cooking was much better." He struck me then, a backhanded blow across my mouth. Blood seeping from one corner of my lips, I met his furious gaze and, in that instant, our relationship was forever severed. I jumped to my feet and ran from the room, from the apartment, from my father. I could hear him calling to me, saying he was sorry, but I kept on running, tears streaming down my face. I was sixteen.

Then I pulled myself together. I was no longer the child I had been before the Nazis came. It was time to be a man.

Over the next few months, my father visited me several times trying to make amends. He invited me back to his home but I refused. On some level I realized that I should be asking his forgiveness for my unkind remark about Ilonka's cooking, but, at this time, all I knew was my own pain and I closed my heart to him. By December 1946, an opportunity came for me to make another run at getting out of Romania. Without saying anything to my father, I and a man I had befriended left Cluj. Forever.

I would never see my father again.

FINDING MYSELF

WE MADE IT to Budapest. Now I was a "displaced person." My friend and I parted. I found a refugee camp run by a Jewish agency and registered. On a list of names of people looking for surviving families, I found my mother's sister's name. I went to her and she took me to another sister and a cousin. Although being with my family again was cause for rejoicing, I still felt the need to move on. I stayed in Budapest for a month, then snuck across the border into Czechoslovakia with ten others and travelled to Bratislava, Czechoslovakia. Three days later, we were smuggled into Austria and we travelled to Salzburg. By crossing the Alps, we tried to reach the American sector but mistakenly walked in a circle and found ourselves back in the Russian sector. The next day, we made it back into the American sector without any problems. Counsellors at a camp fed us, gave us identification papers, accommodations, interviewed us and treated us like human beings. The food and comforts were so good that I could have stayed forever, except I wanted to find my sisters. I asked to go to Landsberg, Germany and was given train passage.

The camp in Landsberg was huge. There was no register to see or a list to look at. Asking around proved unsuccessful. Then I recalled that Lili's husband, Henry, was a camp policeman so I went to the police station and asked there. Sure enough, the policeman on duty led me to Lili and Henry. Sari and Albert had left for Palestine. I had at least found one sister and felt I could make a new life for myself. That thought proved short-lived. In March 1947, Lili and Henry received official documents allowing them to live in France, having been sponsored by Henry's family. Once again I was about to lose my family. Going back to my father was out of the question.

In early May 1947, my sister Lili's family and several other families boarded a train for Paris by way of Munich and Frankfurt. I boarded the train with them to say my goodbyes and returned to the platform fully intending to wave as the train pulled out. When at last it did begin to move, I impulsively jumped back on, thinking I would get off at Frankfurt.

I didn't.

I journeyed with them to Frankfurt. It was there I decided to go all the way. When we got to the French border, I hid under the seat and had it surrounded with baby carriages and crying babies. I stayed hidden long after the train continued until I was certain the customs officers had left. When we arrived in Paris, Henry's family took me to a hostel. I felt safe. But that, too, proved short-lived. The police showed up unexpectedly and asked for documents. I had none. I was arrested and taken to jail along with others who were also in the hostel without documents. My adventure was now becoming a misadventure.

In jail we were questioned and fed. The cell was not locked. Later that afternoon we were released to a French Jewish Agency and given I.D. cards, taken to a train station where we boarded a train for Chelles Gourney, a resort town about an hour away, to a hotel that had been converted to an orphanage. The orphanage held about forty boys. Jobs were available either in town or in Paris. I was able to get a job in town at a small machine shop. On weekends, I returned to Paris to visit with my sister and her family. Again I was able to assume a life. Lili wrote to my father and told him where we were. Having received a letter, he in turn told us what had happened to Sari. She and Albert had tried to go to Palestine on a ship named Ben Hecht and had been caught by the British while trying to enter Haifa. They had been taken to Cyprus where they were to stay for thirteen months, until April 1948.

Again it was decision time for me. I decided to immigrate to the United States, Canada or Australia, to leave the past behind. It was not an easy decision. I've never wanted to be alone and yet I realized I needed to be on my own. I needed to be away from the places where pain and death had entered my life. Or maybe I wanted to put as much distance as possible between my father and me. To put my decision into motion, I needed three copies of my birth certificate. I added a postscript to one of Lili's letters to my father asking him to send me copies of my birth certificate and a few weeks later they arrived. I was now able to go anywhere I wanted. I submitted my application to the three countries and received confirmation from Canada. I was going to Canada.

Canada.

A name on a map.

MY NEW HOME

I SAID MY goodbyes at the rail station in Paris, boarded a train for Calais, then a ferry to Dover, England, then another train to London and finally a train to Southampton, where we boarded the luxury liner SS Aquitania. The time on the ship was a learning experience. I learned how to use a fork and a knife, got seasick and got lost trying to find my way about. On October 6, 1947, seven days after leaving Dover, I arrived in Halifax, Nova Scotia. I was in Canada.

After being processed by immigration, I was placed in a taxi with another boy, Anton Deutsch, and taken to a home. There, talking in Yiddish, I was welcomed to Canada, brought to the dinner table and took part in my first Sabbath meal in the New World.

The next day we were taken to the Jewish "Y", where all the new arrivals gathered. A large map of Canada hung on the wall. An official from the Canadian Jewish Congress, using a pointer, would point to a city and told us they had a fixed number of families willing to take refugees and the number that could go there. He asked for volunteers. When the pointer reached Winnipeg, I, Anton and four others volunteered. We were introduced to Miss Thelma Tessler, the representative from Winnipeg and under her care six of us boarded a train west three days later. There were frequent stops and the journey seemed endless. If we had travelled this far in Europe, we would have passed many cities and crossed many borders, but in Canada all we saw was the occasional small town, snow, more snow and long stretches of uninhabited, rather desolate land. The looks we gave each other were not positive. That night we reached Montreal and changed trains. The next morning we arrived in Toronto. Our car was shunted to another track and added to another train and our journey resumed. It took five days to reach Winnipeg. Who would have thought any one country could be this large? I remembered that Winnipeg was almost in the centre of the country. It was unimaginable to me the length and breadth of our new country.

In Winnipeg we were taken to the homes where we would room and board, two to a home. Anton and I were placed with a poor family who had come years before from Romania and were being paid to accommodate us. The next day we were taken to a large store with the name "Eaton's" on the wall and were allowed to purchase clothes. Within a week I had a job working for Sheffrin Welding & Iron Works, a company owned by a Jewish family, and was paid twenty cents an hour for a sixty-hour week. I thought I would be rich.

After the first month, I had to pay for my room and board, for my cigarettes and streetcar fare. By the weekend, I had no spending money and had to learn the value of a dollar. It didn't take long before my work was appreciated and I got a raise, so I purchased a bicycle to use for going to work. Now I didn't have to spend any money on transportation. Over the next couple of years I moved a few times, each time my financial position improved. I met a Czechoslovakian girl, Brenda Birenbaum, who spoke Hungarian, and it wasn't long before we became engaged. I left all the wedding arrangements with the family who had helped me since my arrival in Winnipeg, only to discover they'd neglected to invite my bosses. This led to a deterioration of my relationship with the Sheffrins and eventually I had to find other employment. I discovered that unless I did it myself, I was asking for trouble. The efforts of others don't always reflect what is in my own best interests. This was a lesson in life that would do me well in the future.

Brenda and I were married on Sunday, March 6, 1949 and we

moved into a flat on Alfred Avenue, in west end Winnipeg. She worked as a hairdresser and I found two jobs. Being married, I learned that two cannot live as cheaply as one. I also entered a Yiddish oratorical contest at the "Y" and won the Feldman Trophy. This became another lesson for the son of the couple who had helped me had been in the contest and the knowledge left me less than elated. I learned that to succeed, it was necessary to extend yourself to do your very best, but in success there was also pain.

Mr. Feldman owned the largest garment factory in Winnipeg. I knew that my friends working in the *shmatta* business were making more money than I. A few weeks after the contest, I went to see him and asked for a job. I told him my father was a tailor and I used to help him. He was skeptical but he called his department supervisor into his office and told him to start me the next day. He placed me in a department and showed me how to operate a power-driven sewing machine. Another lesson. If I want something, go for it.

Within a week I was making enough money to quit my second job. My income soared. A month later, I was promoted and, about a year later, promoted again. I was doing the highest-paid work, assembling the whole jacket. I worked long hours in hopes of bettering, not only my financial position, but also my standing in the community. Long hours means making sacrifices and there comes a time when the sacrifice may be too high a price to pay.

On March 15, 1950, my son, David, was born. By this time, my marriage was on shaky legs. There are many reasons marriages fail. I don't for a moment believe that blame is one-sided. It was a painful period. Within six months of David's birth, we separated. Another lesson. Even the best plans can go astray.

I searched the newspapers for a job well away from my now-painful surroundings and found one as a tool-and-die maker in Fort William (now Thunder Bay) at Canadian Car & Foundry (now Bombardier). I packed my clothes and left Winnipeg the next day. Canadian Car & Foundry was a huge company with more than 1,500 employees and 15 toolmakers. Although I was the youngest, it appeared I had the most experience.

Within a three month period, I had returned to Winnipeg twice. During one of these trips, Brenda and I patched things up and our marriage was back on track. I moved her and my son to my apartment in Fort William. Shortly afterwards, we moved to a better part of the city. All the while, we tried to make the marriage work. It didn't.

In May 1951, I took my suitcase and my tools and boarded a train for Toronto. As soon as I arrived, I bought a newspaper and went to Moffats, an appliance manufacturer, in answer to their ad and was hired. I found a room nearby and began my new job the next day. I was assigned as a helper to a toolmaker with a thick Cockney accent. I had difficulty understanding him and, inevitably, tension heightened between us. After one terrible row, many foul words uttered, I was assigned to a Canadian tool maker.

But this was not a place for me.

Three months later, I started another job at a small tool and die shop called Ajax Precision and learned several new skills. I enjoyed my work very much. I moved into the Jewish area of Toronto, rented a house on Major Street and began proceedings to sponsor my sister Lili and her family to Canada. In the spring of 1953, they arrived. I returned to Fort William twice in hopes of resolving my marital problems. I had asked for David to move back with me. Brenda had a boyfriend and was building a new life. At first she wouldn't agree. She wanted her son to be with her. On my third visit she changed her mind and David came to Toronto with me.

I took a part-time job working in a fruit and vegetable store for the summer. It was fortunate for me that I did, because by November I was let go from the tool-and-die company due to a work shortage. For the first time in my life, I was collecting unemployment insurance. I did odd jobs, one of which was to work at Harbord Fish Market, scaling, gutting and filleting fish. It was slimy, smelly work, but it was work. In February 1954, I started divorce proceedings. That, too, was a lesson. You can't begin fresh until you have put closure to the past. I had done that with my father and now I had to do it with Brenda.

Without a job, I opened a grocery store, uncharted waters for me. It was a mistake. In six months I went out of business and into debt. It took me two years to pay off what I owed. Another lesson. Stay with what you know best. I returned to my trade, tool-and-die. In September 1954, I got a job with Amalgamated Electric Co. and the following month received my Canadian citizenship papers. I was now a Canadian. That same month my divorce petition was heard in the Supreme Court of Ontario and it was granted, but David was to live with his mother. I had lost custody of my son.

My new job though, was very rewarding. My supervisor, Ernie Beaudette, a French Canadian, took me under his wing, coached me and taught me new skills. I realized how badly I lacked a higher education and enrolled at Dominion Business College, a private school. After several years of attending classes two evenings a week, I graduated with my high school diploma. By 1956, I had it made. I had a job, a nice place to live and money in the bank. I could never have imagined that life could be this good when I was digging in tunnels during the war. Whatever lay ahead, I knew I now could face it, and no matter the obstacles, I could overcome. I met Ruth Daniels, a devout Roman Catholic, and fell in love.

There were many obstacles to hurdle. There was anger from both families, prejudices and fears to overcome. The lessons I had learned wouldn't help me now. I was dealing with a different type of situation where honesty and sincerity were not as important as tradition and appearance. Prejudices take time to be built. Sometimes years, sometimes centuries. I knew I could not overcome these prejudices in one swift swoop or break it down. The bridge between Ruth and me was easier to cross than the suspicion and doubts from both families. We were treading on forbidden ground. Two opposing faiths, both opposed to each other, had to be accommodated. The Catholic Church had its rules and my Jewish family had their beliefs. Being Jewish and being religious were two different things with me. The war, the Holocaust, the scenes I had witnessed had scarred me, destroyed my faith in God. But that I was a Jew I never doubted. Ruth was as fixed in her beliefs as I was in mine. That meant compromise. After much soul-searching, I made my concessions. On November 16, 1957, we were married at the Holy Name Church at Danforth and Pape. And then another good thing. Brenda allowed David to live with us.

In September 1959, Mary Anne was born. In April 1961, Jacqueline Marie. In March 1964, Karen Elizabeth. Over the next years, there were many changes in my life, more jobs, school, a new home, investments and a new goal – to own my own company. Brenda remarried and moved to Cleveland. David went with her. They then moved to Los Angeles and it was too hard for me to see David. Occasional business sent me west; sometimes I saw David, other times he was unavailable. Late spring of 1966, while I was in Chicago on business, I received an urgent call from Ruth. Brenda had phoned, she said, to tell me that David had run away and the police found him in St. Louis, Missouri and held him in custody. I dropped what I was doing and flew to St. Louis and had him released. We returned to Toronto and David stayed with us about a year before returning to Los Angeles. In late 1968, he again returned to Toronto to finish his secondary education.

On October 1969, I opened my own business, which I called Tooling Enterprises Ltd. By 1971, I expanded into two units and applied for a blanket patent covering twenty-five inventions for a tooling system I had designed and developed.

In 1972, I travelled to Israel to visit my sister Sari whom I hadn't seen for twenty-five years. Her marriage to Albert had failed and she had remarried. Seeing Sari was only one reason for my coming to Israel. The other was my father. He was buried in Tel Aviv. Sari took me to his grave. He had died in March 1951 after being in Israel only a few weeks. I gazed at the monument and tried to feel something, anything, to put closure to what had happened between my father and me. But there was nothing. I said a prayer and left. Sari told me that during the period of mourning, they awoke one morning to find that Ilonka (his wife) was gone. She never returned and no one has heard from her again.

What else is there to tell? My family and I prospered. My business grew. I opened another plant in Buffalo. My children turned into adults and my forty-four year marriage remained as strong as ever. I am now over 70 and in the twilight of my life. I survived great horrors and managed to build a new life. I have set down roots in a country that has given me a wife, children, prosperity and the knowledge that, in the years to come, my children and their grandchildren will accomplish whatever goals they set for themselves. The horrors are behind me. And I see only sunlight ahead.